The
LITTLE
BLACK
SONGBOOK
Ed
Sheeran

HAL•LEONARD®
CORPORATION
7777 W. BLUEMOUND RD. P.O. BOX 13819 MILWAUKEE, WI 53213

THE A TEAM

Words & Music by Ed Sheeran

Capo second fret

Intro
| G | G | G | G D/F♯ |
| Em | Em C | G | G ‖

Verse 1

     G   D/F♯   Em
White lips, pale face, breathing in snowflakes,

           C   G
Burnt lungs, sour taste.

                                    D/F♯   Em
Light's gone, day's end, struggling to pay rent,

                C   G
Long nights, strange men.

Chorus 1

Am⁷   C
And they say she's in the class A team,

               G   D
Stuck in her daydream, been this way since eighteen.

                 Am⁷   C
But lately her face seems slowly sinking, wasting,

                 G
Crumbling like pastries. And they scream

     D
The worst things in life come free to us.

              Em   C
'Cause we're just under the upper hand

G
    And go mad for a couple grams,

Em   C   G
    And she don't want to go outside   tonight.

cont.

        Em   **C**
And in a pipe she flies to the Motherland

G
   Or sells love to another man.

Em   **C**   **G**   **D**   **Em C G**
  It's too cold   outside   for angels to fly,

          Em C G
Angels to fly.

Verse 2

G   **D**   **Em**
Ripped gloves, raincoat, tried to swim and stay afloat,

        C   **G**
Dry house, wet clothes.

                           D   **Em**
Loose change, bank notes, weary-eyed, dry throat,

        C   **G**
Call girl, no phone.

Chorus 2

Am7   **C**
And they say she's in the class A team,

        G   **D**
Stuck in her daydream, been this way since eighteen.

         Am7   **C**
But lately her face seems slowly sinking, wasting,

        G
Crumbling like pastries. And they scream

D
The worst things in life come free to us.

           Em   **C**
'Cause we're just under the upper hand

G
   And go mad for a couple grams,

Em   **C**   **G**
  And she don't want to go outside   tonight.

        Em   **C**
And in a pipe she flies to the Motherland

G
   Or sells love to another man.

Em   **C**   **G**   **Am7**
  It's too cold   outside   for angels to fly.

Bridge

Am7   C   Em
That angel will die covered in white,

        G
Closed eye and hoping for a better life.

Am7   C
This time, we'll fade out tonight,

         (Em)
Straight down the line.

Instrumental ‖: Em | C | G | G   :‖

Chorus 3

Am7   C
And they say she's in the class A team,

       G   D
Stuck in her daydream, been this way since eighteen.

         Am7   C
But lately her face seems slowly sinking, wasting,

          G
Crumbling like pastries. And they scream

     D
The worst things in life come free to us.

       Em   C
And we're all under the upper hand

G
  And go mad for a couple grams,

Em   C   G
  And we don't want to go outside tonight.

       Em   C
And in the pipe fly to the Motherland

G
  Or sell love to another man.

Em   C   G D   Em C G
  It's too cold outside for angels to fly,

      Em C G
Angels to fly,___

     Em C   G
To fly,___ fly,___

        Em C   G
For angels to fly, to fly, to fly,

D   G
Angels to die.

AFIRE LOVE

Words & Music by Ed Sheeran,
Foy Vance, Christophe Beck & Johnny McDaid

Dm   B♭   Gm   C   F   F/A   B♭6

Intro ‖: **Dm** | **B♭** | **Gm** | **C** :‖ *Play 3 times*

Verse 1

Dm
Things were all good yesterday,
                                    B♭
And then the devil took your memory.

And if you fell to your death today,
                              Dm
I hope that heaven is your resting place.
                              F
I heard the doctor put your chest in pain,
                              Gm
But then that could've been the medicine.
                              C
And now you're lying in the bed again,
                              B♭
Either way I'll cry with the rest of them.

Pre-chorus 1

B♭   **F/A**   **Dm**
   And my father told me, son,
        B♭   **F**
It's not his fault he doesn't know your face.
B♭   **F/A**   **Dm**
   And you're not the only one,
            B♭   **C**
Although my grandma used to say

He used to sing:

11

Chorus 1

Dm   B♭   B♭6
Darling, hold me in your arms the way you did last night,

                C
And we'll lie in - side for a little while, here, oh.

Dm   B♭   B♭6
I could look into your eyes until the sun comes up,

                C   Dm
And we're wrapped in light, in life, and love.

                  B♭   B♭6
Put your open lips on mine and slowly let them shut,

              C
For they're de - signed to be together, oh.

Dm   B♭   B♭6
With your body next to mine our hearts will beat as one,

              C   Dm
And we're set a - light, we're afire love.

Link | Dm | B♭ | Gm | C   ‖

Verse 2

Dm
Things were all good yesterday,

                          B♭
Then the devil took your breath a - way.

And now we're left with the pain,

Black suit, black tie, standing in the rain.

Dm   F
And now my family is one again,

                                           Gm
Stapled all together with the strangers and a friend.

                                      C
Came to my mind, I should paint it with a pen,

Six years old, I remember when.

Pre-chorus 2   As Pre-chorus 1

Chorus 2   As Chorus 1

Dm   B♭   B♭6
  Love,___ love.

                                  C
It's in the love, the love, the love, the love.

Dm   B♭
  It's in the love, the love, the love, the love.

B♭6   C
  It's in the love, the love, the love, the love.

          Dm   B♭
And my father and all of my family

              B♭6   C
Rise from these seats to sing "Hallelu - jah."

          Dm   B♭
And my mother and all of my family

              B♭6   C
Rise from these seats to sing "Hallelu - jah."

          Dm   B♭
And my brother and all of my family

              B♭6   C
Rise from these seats to sing "Hallelu - jah."

          Dm   B♭
And my father and all of my family

              B♭6   C
Rise from these seats to sing "Hallelu - jah."

Dm B♭ B♭6   C
           It's in the love, the love, the love, the love.

Dm   B♭
  It's in the love, the love, the love, the love.

B♭6   C
  It's in the love, the love, the love, the love.

Outro   ‖: Dm | B♭ | B♭6 | C   :‖ *Play 3 times*

ALL OF THE STARS

Words & Music by Ed Sheeran & Johnny McDaid

E   B   G#m   B/F#   F#   Bmaj7
fr4

Verse 1

    E   B   G#m B/F# E
It's just another night   and I'm sta - ring   at the moon,
    B   F#
I saw a shooting star   and thought of you.
    E   B   G#m B/F# E
I sang a lullaby   by the wa - ter - side and knew
    B   F#
If you were here, I'd sing to you.
    E   B   G#m B/F# E   B
You're on the other side   as the sky - line   splits in two,
                      F#
Miles away from seeing you.
    E   B   G#m B/F# E
But I can see the stars   from A - me - ri - ca,
    B   F#
I wonder, do you see them too?

Chorus 1

    N.C.   B
So open your eyes and see
              F#
The way our ho - rizons meet.
           G#m
And all of the lights will lead
        E
Into the night with me.
           B
And I know these scars will bleed,
              F#
But both of our hearts believe
       G#m   E   B   F#
All of these stars will guide___ us home.

Verse 2

```
E                              B      G♯m B/F♯  E
     I can hear your heart    on the ra - di - o beat,
B                                  F♯
     They're playing "Chasing Cars" and I thought of us.
E                      B      G♯m B/F♯ E
     Back to the time    you were ly - ing next to me
B                        F♯
     I looked across and fell in love.
E                          B              G♯m    B/F♯  E
     So I took your hand    back through lamp - lit    streets and knew
B                        F♯
     Everything led back to you.
E                          B              G♯m   B/F♯    E
     So can you see the    stars over Am - ster - dam,
B                              F♯
     Hear the song my heart is beating to?
```

Chorus 2   As Chorus 1

Outro

```
          E    F♯
And oh,____
          G♯m  Bmaj7
And oh,_____
          E    F♯  B
And oh,_____
E                          B          G♯m  B/F♯ E
     I can see the stars    from A - me - ri - ca.
```

AUTUMN LEAVES

Words & Music by Ed Sheeran & Jake Gosling

Em7   D/F#   G   C   D(add4)   Em   A7sus2

Capo third fret

Intro | Em7 D/F# | G C | Em7 D/F# | G C   ‖

Verse 1
        Em7   D/F#   G   C   Em7
        Another day,   another life   passes by___ just like mine,
                 D/F#   G C
        It's not complicated.
        Em7   D/F#   G   C   Em7
        Another mind,   another soul   another body to grow old,
                 D/F#   G C
        It's not complicated.

Pre-chorus 1
        C   D(add4)
        Do you ever wonder if the stars shine out for you?

Chorus 1
        G   D/F#   Em   C
        Float   down   like Autumn leaves,
        G   D/F# Em   C
        And hush now, close your eyes be - fore the sleep.
        G   D/F#   Em
        And you're miles away,___
                 C   G D/F#   Em   C
        And yesterday   you were here with me.

Link 1 | Em7 D/F# | G C | Em7 D/F# | G C   ‖

16

Em7   D/F♯   G   C   Em7
 Another tear, another cry, another place for us to die,

    D/F♯   G C
It's not complicated.

Em7   D/F♯   G   C   Em7
 Another life that's gone to waste, another light lost from your face,

   D/F♯   G C
It's complicated.

C   D(add4)
 Is it that it's over or do birds still sing for you?

  As Chorus 1

A7sus2   C
  Ooh, how I miss you,

   G   D/F♯
My symphony played the song that carried you out.

A7sus2   C
 Ooh, how I miss you,

   G   D/F♯
And I, I miss you and I wish you'd stay.

  As Pre-chorus 1

  As Chorus 1

Em7   D/F♯   G   C
  Ooh, ooh, ooh, ooh, ooh, ooh, ooh, ooh.

Em7   D/F♯   G   C
 Ooh, ooh, ooh, ooh, ooh, ooh, ooh, ooh.

G   D/F♯ Em C
  Touch down like a seven four seven,

G   D/F♯ Em   A7sus2
 We'll stay out and we'll live forever now.

BARCELONA

Words & Music by Ed Sheeran, Benjamin Levin,
John McDaid, Foy Vance & Amy Wadge

G/D   D   Bsus4   Bm7   Asus4   A
D/G   A/G   D/A   D/B   D*   G/A

Chords written as if Drop D tuning

⑥ = Db   ③ = Gb
⑤ = Ab   ② = Bb
④ = Db   ① = Eb

Intro
| G/D   D | Bsus4 Bm7 | Asus4 A | D/G |

| G/D   D | Bsus4 Bm7 | Asus4 A |

Verse 1
       D/G N.C.   D   Bm7
Well, get   up up on the dance floor tonight,
                A   D/G
I've got two left feet and a bottle of red wine,
           D   Bm7
Making me feel like the beat and the bass-line
        A   D/G
Are in my blood, both hands upon her waistline.
        D   Bm7
Get on up baby, dance to the rhythm of the music,
A   D/G
Don't care what the DJ chooses.
D   Bm7
  Get lost in the rhythm of me,
A   D/G
Place don't close until we wanna leave it.

Pre-chorus 1
    D/G   A/G A D/A   D/B   D*
    You   and I we're flying on an aeroplane tonight,
    D/G   A/G A D/A D/B   D*
      We're going,   somewhere where the sun is shining bright.
    D/G   A/G G/A D/A   D/B   D*
      Just close_____ your eyes,
          D/G   D/A
And let's pretend we're dancing in the street.

Chorus 1

| | N.C. | G/D | D | Bsus⁴ | Bm⁷ | Asus⁴ | A | D/G |

Chorus 1

N.C.   G/D D Bsus^4 Bm^7 Asus^4 A   D/G
In Barcelona.
                      G/D D Bsus^4 Bm^7 Asus^4 A   D/G
Barcelona.
                      G/D D Bsus^4 Bm^7 Asus^4 A   D/G
Barcelona.
                      G/D D Bsus^4 Bm^7 Asus^4 A
Barcelona.

Verse 2

          D/G N.C.   D   Bm^7
Well, get up up on the dance floor, move, it's a Saturday night,
A   D/G
I fell in love with the sparkle in the moonlight
D   Bm^7
  Reflected in your beautiful eyes,
  A   D/G
I guess that is destiny doing it right.
        D   N.C.
And dance like they do in the Mediterranean,
  D   N.C.
Spin you around me again and again and
D   Bm^7
You're like something that God has sent me,
N.C.
I want you baby, solamente.

Pre-chorus 2 as Pre-chorus 1

Chorus 2

N.C.   G/D D Bsus^4 Bm^7 Asus^4 A   D/G
In Barcelona.
                      G/D D Bsus^4 Bm^7 Asus^4 A   D/G
Barcelona.
                      G/D D Bsus^4 Bm^7 Asus^4 A   D/G
Barcelona.
                      G/D D Bsus^4 Bm^7 Asus^4 A   D/G
Barcelona.
N.C.
Barcelona.

Pre-chorus 3 | D/G   A/G | G/A   D/A | D/B |

        | **D*** | D/G   A/G | G/A   D/A | D/B |
        Barcelona
        | **D*** | D/G   A/G | G/A   D/A | D/B |
        Oh, Barcelona.
          D/G   D/A
      So let's pretend we're dancing in the street in Barcelona.

        D   Bm7   A   D/G
Outro   Las Ramblas,   I'll meet you, we'll dance around La Sagrada Familia.
        D   Bm7   A   D/G
      Drinking   Sangria, mi niña, te amo mi cariño.
        D   Bm7   A   D/G
      Mamacita,   rica, si tú,   te adoro señorita.
        D   Bm7   A   D/G
      Los otros,   viva la vida.   Come on let's be free in Barcelona.
        D   Bm7   A   D/G
      Las Ramblas,   I'll meet ya,   come on and dance with me, in Barcelo
        D   Bm7   A   D/G
      Drinking   Sangria, I just want to be in Barcelona.
        D   Bm7   A   D/G
     Mamacita,   rica,   feel that summer breeze in Barcelona.
        D   Bm7   A   D/G
      Los otros,   viva la vida,   siempre vida Barcelona.

BE LIKE YOU

Words & Music by Ed Sheeran

G   B7   Em   C   Am7   Dadd9/F♯   Dadd4   Dadd4/F♯

Capo 4

Intro   ‖: G | B7 | Em | C   :‖

Verse 1
```
        G      B7      Em C    G     B7    Em  C
        And happy days_____ that left us on the floor,
        G      B7      Em   C   G        B7    Em   C
        And you squeeze__ me__ till you're not feeling sure.
        G                 B7            Em           C
        Everything will brighten up if we go to Brighton,
            G       B7      Em     C
        I'll take you along the Pier.
        G                 B7            Em              C
        Everything will lighten up and  if you feel too frightened,
            G       B7      Em  C
        I'll make things disappear,     dear.
```

Pre-chorus 1
```
        Am7              C
        Darling, don't be nervous,
        G         Dadd9/F♯
        I'll understand if you let me go.
        Am7        C           G    Dadd9/F♯
        I did this on purpose, now,_____
                    B7
        'Cause when I'm missing you
```

Chorus 1
```
        Em               Am7              C
        I'll stop eating food    and I'll squeeze into a dress
                        G         Dadd4      B7
        So I can be like you.   And then I'll see your bitterness
        Em                    Am7              C
        And why you're leaving too,   maybe I'll put you to a test
                        G           Dadd4
        And say that I love you,    I think that I love you.
```

Verse 2

G   B7   Em   C   G   B7   Em   C
And sunny days____that left my skin dark red,

G   B7   Em   C   G   B7   Em   C
And you breathe___ me till these thoughts leave my head.

G   B7   Em   C
If it gets too complicated,   I'll give up and be frustrated

G   B7   Em   C
Can you see what's wrong?

G   B7   Em   C
If you feel like you've been jaded and this love's too overrated,

G   B7   Em C
See what's going on.__

Pre-chorus 2

Am7   C
Darling, don't be nervous,

G   Dadd9/F♯
I'll understand if you let me go.

Am7   C   G   Dadd4/F♯
I did this on purpose, now,_____

                 B7
'Cause when I'm missing you

Chorus 2

Em   Am7   C
I'll stop eating food   and I'll squeeze into a dress

                G   Dadd4   (B7)
So I can be like you.   And then I'll see your bitterness

Em   Am7   C
And why you're leaving too,   maybe I'll put you to a test

                G   Dadd4
And say that I love you,   I think that I love you.

Pre-chorus 3

Am7   C   G   Dadd4/F♯
Take me back to live at home,_____

Am7   C   G   Dadd4
Take me back to Albert Road._____

               B7
'Cause when I'm missing you.

```
   Em                    Am7                        C
     I'll stop eating food    and I'll squeeze into your dress
                      G            Dadd4        B7
   So I can feel like you.   And then I'll see your bitterness
   Em                        Am7                      C
     And why you left me too,     I thought I'd put you to a test
                      G            Dadd4   B7
   And say that I love you,   I think that I love you.
```

```
   Em                    Am7                          C
     And I'll stop eating food    and I'll squeeze into your dress
                      G            Dadd4        B7
   So I can feel like you.   And then I'll see your bitterness
   Em                        Am7                      C
     And why you left me too,     I thought I put you to a test
                      G            Dadd4                  G
   And say that I love you,   now it seems you loved me too.____
```

BIBIA BE YE YE

Words & Music by Ed Sheeran, Joseph Addison,
Benjamin Levin, Nana Abiona & Stephen Woode

Capo 5

Intro | D | Em7 | G | A |

D Em7 G   A
      Bibia be ye ye.

‖: D | Em7 | G | A   :‖

Verse 1
    D   Em7   G   A   D
    I lost my shoes last night, I don't know where I put my keys,
Em7   G   A   D
    I was tired and fell asleep beneath an oak tree.
Em7   G   A   D   Em7
    I bet my mother's proud of me from each scar upon my knuckle
        G   A   D
And each graze upon my knee. And all I know
Em7   G   A   D
    Is I got a cab and then threw up on his car seat,
Em7   G   A   D
    He kicked me out and then I walked in the rain.
Em7   G   A   D   Em7
    I tell myself in every way I won't be doing this again
        G   A
And tomorrow's a brand new day.

Chorus 1
    D   Em7   G   A
    Someone told me,   always say what's on your mind,
D   Em7 G   A
   And I am only   being honest with you.
D   Em7   G   A
I, I get lonely   and make mistakes from time to time,
D   Em7   G   A
  Se enioma enko   ye, bibia be ye ye.
D   Em7 G   A   D   Em7
     Bibia be ye ye ye ye ye ye ye,
G   A
  Bibia be ye ye.

```
D    Em7            G              A            D
     I remember less and less and mostly things that I regret,
         Em7            G         A            D
     In my phone are several texts from girls I've never met.
             Em7        G          A            D
     And in the pocket of my jeans are only coins and broken dreams,
             Em7        G              A
     My heart is breaking at the seams and I'm coming apart now.
     D              Em7          G            A            D
        Now things are looking up, I'll find my shoes right next to the oak tree,
     Em7          G              A
        And I'll get a bus straight into town
         D                 Em7                    G
     And spend the afternoon looking around for the things
                     A
            that I left on the ground,
         D                 Em7   G          A
     And say you're with me, tomorrow's a brand new day.
```

```
     D          Em7   G            A
        Someone told me, always say what's on your mind,
     D          Em7 G       A
        And I am only   being honest with you.
     D      Em7  G            A
     I, I get lonely  and make mistakes from time to time,
     D              Em7   G     A
        Se enioma enko ye,   bibia  be ye ye.
```

```
     D              Em7  G            A
        Wo nooma,         wo nooma ma ye.
     D              Em7  G            A
        Wo nooma,         wo nooma ma ye.
     D              Em7  G            A
        Wo nooma,       wo nooma ma ye.
     D              Em7  G            A
        Wo nooma,         wo nooma ma ye.
```

Chorus 3

D   Em⁷   G   A
  Someone told me,   always say what's on your mind,

D   Em⁷ G   A
  And I am only   being honest with you.

D   Em⁷ G   A
I, I get lonely and make mistakes from time to time,

D   Em⁷ G   A
  Se enioma enko ye, bibia be ye ye.

D Em⁷ G   A   D   Em⁷
          Bibia be ye ye ye ye ye ye ye,

G   A
  Bibia be ye ye.

D Em⁷ G   A   D   Em⁷
          Bibia be ye ye ye ye ye ye ye,

G   A
  Bibia be ye.

Link 2   ‖: D | Em⁷ | G | A   :‖

Outro

D   Em⁷ G   A
  Wo nooma,   wo nooma ma ye.

D   Em⁷ G   A   D
  Wo nooma,   wo nooma ma ye.

CASTLE ON THE HILL

Words & Music by Ed Sheeran & Benjamin Levin

D5 **D** **D/F♯** **G** **Bm7** **Asus4** **Dmaj7/F♯**

Intro
| D5 | D5 | D5 | D5 |

Verse 1

D   D/F♯   G   Bm7   Asus4
When I was six years old I broke my leg.

D   D/F♯   G   Bm7   Asus4
I was running from my brother and his friends

D   D/F♯   G   Bm7   Asus4
And tasted the sweet perfume of the mountain grass I rolled down.

D   D/F♯ G   Bm7   Asus4
I was younger then,   take me back to when

Pre-chorus 1

G   Asus4   D
I found my heart and broke it here,

                   G
Made friends and lost them through the years.

           Asus4   D
And I've not seen the roaring fields in so long,

G   Asus4
I know I've grown, but I can't wait to go home.

Chorus 1

D   D/F♯   G   Bm7   Asus4
I'm on my   way, driving at ninety

         D   D/F♯ G   Bm7   Asus4
Down those country   lanes singing to 'Tiny Dancer.'

      D   D/F♯   Bm7   Asus4
And I miss the way__ you make   me feel,   and it's real

         D   D/F♯ G   Bm7   Asus4
When we watched the   sunset over the castle on the hill.

Link 1
| D5 | D5 | |

Verse 2

```
           D        D/F♯  G                      Bm7                        Asus4
           Fifteen years  old and smoking hand-rolled cigarettes.
           D                    D/F♯    G
           Running from the law—through the backfields
             Bm7              Asus4
           and getting drunk with my friends.
           D        D/F♯ G              Bm7          Asus4              D
           Had my first kiss on a Friday night, I don't reckon that I did it right,
                    D/F♯  G  Bm7              Asus4
           I was younger   then,   take me back to when
```

Pre-chorus 2

```
           (Asus4)   G          Asus4            D
           We found    weekend jobs, when we got paid
                              G
           We'd buy cheap spirits and drink them straight.
                      Asus4                   D
           Me and my friends have not thrown up in so long,
           G                              Asus4
           Oh, how we've grown, but I can't wait to go home.
```

Chorus 2

```
           D        D/F♯ G    Bm7        Asus4
           I'm on my    way, driving at ninety
                  D             D/F♯ G    Bm7          Asus4
           Down those country   lanes singing to 'Tiny Dancer'.
                  D        D/F♯    G        Bm7        Asus4
           And I miss the way—you make   me feel,     and it's real
                  D              D/F♯G     Bm7     Asus4
           When we watched  the  sunset over the castle on the hill.
           D        D/F♯ G  Bm7        Asus4
           Ooh,___ ooh, over the castle on the hill.
           D        D/F♯ G  Bm7        Asus4
           Ooh,___ ooh, over the castle on the hill.
```

Link 2

```
           | Bm7      | G        | D        | Asus4       |
```

Bm7   **G**
One friend left to sell clothes,
D   **Asus4**
One works down by the coast.
Bm7   **G**
One had two kids but lives alone,
D   **Asus4**
One's brother overdosed.
Bm7   **G**
One's already on his second wife,
D   **Asus4**
One's just barely getting by.
    Bm7   **G**
But   these people raised me
       D   **Asus4**
And I__ can't wait to go home.

Chorus 3

     D   **Dmaj7/F♯ G**   **Bm7**   **Asus4**
And I'm on my   way, I still remember
     D   **Dmaj7/F♯ G**   **Bm7**   **Asus4**
These old country   lanes when we did not know the answers.
     D   **D/F♯**   **G**   **Bm7**   **Asus4**
And I miss the way__ you make   me feel,   and it's real
       D   **D/F♯ G**   **Bm7**   **Asus4**
When we watched the   sunset over the castle on the hill.
D   **D/F♯ G**   **Bm7**   **Asus4**
Ooh,___ ooh, over the castle on the hill.
D   **D/F♯ G**   **Bm7**   **Asus4**   **D5**
Ooh,___ ooh, over the castle on the hill.

BLOODSTREAM

Words & Music by Ed Sheeran, Gary Lightbody, John McDaid,
Kesi Dryden, Piers Aggett & Amir Izadkhah

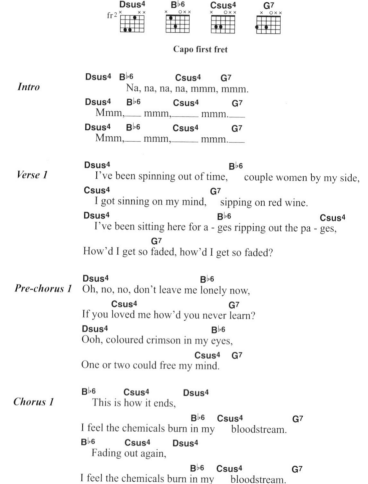

Capo first fret

Intro

Dsus⁴ B♭6 Csus⁴ G⁷
Na, na, na, na, mmm, mmm.

Dsus⁴ B♭6 Csus⁴ G⁷
Mmm,___ mmm,_____ mmm.___

Dsus⁴ B♭6 Csus⁴ G⁷
Mmm,___ mmm,_____ mmm.___

Verse 1

Dsus⁴ B♭6
I've been spinning out of time, couple women by my side,

Csus⁴ G⁷
I got sinning on my mind, sipping on red wine.

Dsus⁴ B♭6 Csus⁴
I've been sitting here for a - ges ripping out the pa - ges,

G⁷
How'd I get so faded, how'd I get so faded?

Pre-chorus 1

Dsus⁴ B♭6
Oh, no, no, don't leave me lonely now,

Csus⁴ G⁷
If you loved me how'd you never learn?

Dsus⁴ B♭6
Ooh, coloured crimson in my eyes,

Csus⁴ G⁷
One or two could free my mind.

Chorus 1

B♭6 Csus⁴ Dsus⁴
This is how it ends,

B♭6 Csus⁴ G⁷
I feel the chemicals burn in my bloodstream.

B♭6 Csus⁴ Dsus⁴
Fading out again,

B♭6 Csus⁴ G⁷
I feel the chemicals burn in my bloodstream.

N.C.   **Dsus⁴**   **B♭6**   **Csus⁴**   **G⁷**
So tell me when it kicks in,   mmm,___ mmm,_____ mmm.___

            Dsus⁴   **B♭6**   **Csus⁴**   **G⁷**
Well, tell me when it kicks in,   mmm,___ mmm,_____ mmm.___

Verse 2

Dsus⁴   **B♭6**   **Csus⁴**
    I've been looking for a lov - er, thought I'd find her in a bot - tle,

                     G⁷
God, make me another one,   I'll be feeling this tomorrow.

Dsus⁴   **B♭6**
Lord, forgive me for the things I've done,

                    Csus⁴
I was never meant to hurt no one,

                  G⁷
And I saw scars upon a   broken-hearted lover.

Pre-chorus 2   As Pre-chorus 1

Chorus 2   As Chorus 1

Bridge

(G⁷)
Well, tell me when it kicks in.

B♭6   **Csus⁴**   **Dsus⁴**   **B♭6**
    All the voices in my mind calling out across the line.

      Csus⁴   **Dsus⁴**   **B♭6**
All the voices in my mind calling out across the line.

      Csus⁴   **Dsus⁴**   **B♭6**
‖: All the voices in my mind calling out across the line.

      Csus⁴   **Dsus⁴**   **B♭6**
All the voices in my mind calling out across the line. :‖

   Csus⁴   **Dsus⁴**   **B♭6**
‖: Tell me when it kicks in,   and I saw scars upon her.

Csus⁴   **Dsus⁴**   **B♭6**
Tell me when it kicks in,   broken - hearted. :‖ *Play 4 times*

Outro

B♭6   **Csus⁴**   **Dsus⁴**   **B♭6**
    Tell me when it kicks in,   and I saw scars upon her.

Csus⁴   **Dsus⁴**   **B♭6**
Tell me when it kicks in,   broken - hearted.

Csus⁴   **Dsus⁴**   **B♭6**
Tell me when it kicks in,   and I saw scars upon her.

Csus⁴   **Dsus⁴**   **N.C.**
Tell me when it kicks in,   broken - hearted.

THE CITY

Words & Music by Ed Sheeran & Jake Gosling

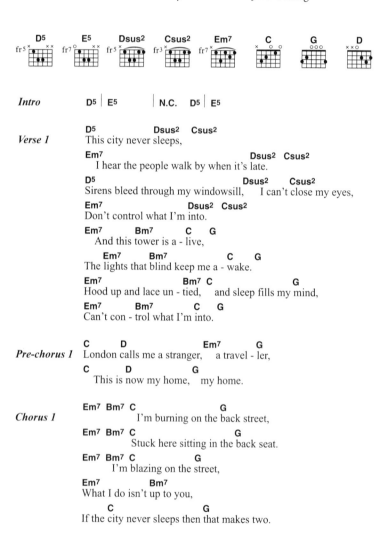

Intro   D5 │ E5   │ N.C.   D5 │ E5

Verse 1
          D5   Dsus2   Csus2
          This city never sleeps,
              Em7   Dsus2   Csus2
              I hear the people walk by when it's late.
          D5   Dsus2   Csus2
          Sirens bleed through my windowsill,   I can't close my eyes,
          Em7   Dsus2   Csus2
          Don't control what I'm into.
          Em7   Bm7   C   G
              And this tower is a - live,
              Em7   Bm7   C   G
          The lights that blind keep me a - wake.
          Em7   Bm7 C   G
          Hood up and lace un - tied,   and sleep fills my mind,
          Em7   Bm7   C   G
          Can't con - trol what I'm into.

Pre-chorus 1
          C   D   Em7   G
          London calls me a stranger,   a travel - ler,
          C   D   G
              This is now my home,   my home.

Chorus 1
          Em7 Bm7 C   G
                      I'm burning on the back street,
          Em7 Bm7 C   G
                      Stuck here sitting in the back seat.
          Em7 Bm7 C   G
              I'm blazing on the street,
          Em7   Bm7
          What I do isn't up to you,
                   C   G
          If the city never sleeps then that makes two.

Link 1   D5 | E5 | N.C.   D5 | E5

Verse 2

Em7   Bm7   C   G
  The pavement is my___ friend,

Em7   Bm7   C   G
  It will take me where I need to go.

Em7   Bm7   C   G
I find it trips me up   and puts me down,

Em7   Bm7   C   G
This is not what I'm used to.

Em7   Bm7   C   G
  And the shop across the road

Em7   Bm7   C   G
  Fills my needs and gives me company when I need it.

Em7   Bm7
Voices speak through my walls,

C   G   Bm7   C G
  I don't think I'm gonna make it past to - morrow.___

Pre-chorus 2   As Pre-chorus 1

Chorus 2   As Chorus 1

Bridge

Em   G
  And my lungs hurt   and my ears bled

Am   C
  With the sound of the city life   echoed in my head.

Em   G
  Do I need this   to keep me alive?

Am   C
The traffic stops and starts but I   need to move along.

Chorus 3

C   D   Em7 G
  London calls me a stranger,___

C   D   G
  And this is not my home, home.

Chorus 4   As Chorus 1

33

COLD COFFEE

Words & Music by Ed Sheeran & Amy Wadge

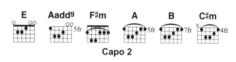

Capo 2

Verse 1
           E
    She's like cold coffee in the morning,
Aadd⁹   E
      I'm drunk off last night's whisky and coke.

She'll make me shiver without warning,
Aadd⁹
And make me laugh as if I'm in on the joke.
          F♯m   **A**   **E**
And you can stay with me forever,
          F♯m   **A**   **B**
Or you could stay with me for now.

Chorus 1
    (B)   **C♯m**   **Aadd⁹**   **E**
And tell me if I'm wrong, and tell me if I'm right,
             F♯m   **A**   **E**
And tell me if you need a loving hand to help you fall asleep tonight.
        C♯m   **Aadd⁹** **E**
And tell me if I know, and tell me if I do,
          F♯m   **A**   **E**
And tell me how to fall in love the way you want me to.

Verse 2
    E
    I'll wake with coffee in the morning,
Aadd⁹   E
      But she prefers two lumps of sugar and tea.

Outside the day is up and calling,
Aadd⁹
      But I don't have to be so, please go back to sleep.
F♯m   **A**   **E**
Stay with me forever,
          F♯m   **A**   **B**
Or you could stay with me for now.

Chorus 2 as Chorus 1

         (E)   B   A   E
Bridge   'Cause I love the way you wake me up.
           B   A   B
         For goodness sake will my love not be enough?

Chorus 3 as Chorus 1

         (E)   C♯m   Aadd⁹   E
Chorus 4   And tell me if I'm wrong, and tell me if I'm right,
                           F♯m   A   E
         And tell me if you need a loving hand to help you fall asleep tonight.

DIVE

Words & Music by Ed Sheeran, Benjamin Levin & Julia Michaels

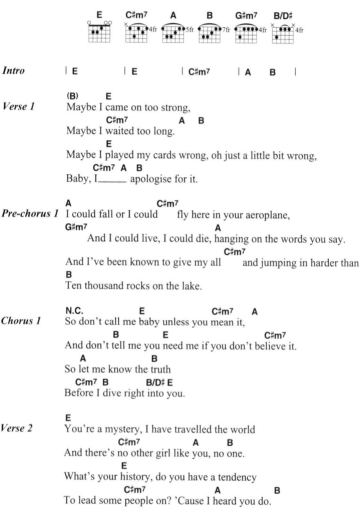

Intro | E | E | C#m7 | A B |

Verse 1
(B)   E
Maybe I came on too strong,
       C#m7   A B
Maybe I waited too long.
       E
Maybe I played my cards wrong, oh just a little bit wrong,
      C#m7 A B
Baby, I_____ apologise for it.

Pre-chorus 1
   A   C#m7
I could fall or I could   fly here in your aeroplane,
 G#m7   A
     And I could live, I could die, hanging on the words you say.
                              C#m7
And I've been known to give my all   and jumping in harder than
B
Ten thousand rocks on the lake.

Chorus 1
N.C.   E   C#m7   A
So don't call me baby unless you mean it,
           B   E   C#m7
And don't tell me you need me if you don't believe it.
  A   B
So let me know the truth
   C#m7 B   B/D# E
Before I dive right into you.

Verse 2
     E
You're a mystery, I have travelled the world
          C#m7   A   B
And there's no other girl like you, no one.
         E
What's your history, do you have a tendency
       C#m7   A   B
To lead some people on? 'Cause I heard you do.

36

                    A   C#m7
Pre-chorus 2 I could fall or I could fly   here in your aeroplane,
                G#m7   A
                    And I could live, I could die, hanging on the words you say.
                                              C#m7
                And I've been known to give my all   and lie awake every day,
                B
                Don't know how much I can take.

Chorus 2 as Chorus 1

Instrumental | E | E | C#m7 | A   B |

                | E | E | C#m7 | A   B |

                    A   C#m7
Pre-chorus 3 I could fall or I could fly   here in your aeroplane,
                G#m7   A
                    And I could live, I could die, hanging on the words you say.
                                          C#m7
                I've been known to give my all,   sitting back,
                                B
                Looking at every mess that I made.

                N.C.   E   C#m7   A
Chorus 3   So don't call me baby unless you mean it,
                                B   E   C#m7
                And don't tell me you need me if you don't believe it.
                        A   B
                So let me know the truth
                    C#m7 B   B/D# E
                Before I dive right into you.
                    C#m7 B   B/D# E
                Before I dive right into you.
                    C#m7 B   B/D# E
                Before I dive right into you.

DRUNK

Words & Music by Ed Sheeran & Jake Gosling

G	G/F♯	Em7	C(add9)	D	Am7	Em

Intro | G | G ‖

Verse 1

G
   I wanna be drunk when I wake up
                  G/F♯ Em7
On the right side of the wrong bed,

And never an excuse I made up,
                      C(add9)
Tell you the truth I hate what   didn't kill me,
                     D   G
It never made me strong - er at all.

Love will scar your make-up, lips sticks to me,
         G/F♯   Em7
So now I maybe lean back there.
                       C(add9)
I'm sat here wishing I was sober,___
                    D   G
I know I'll never hold you like I used to.___

Pre-chorus 1

(G) Em7   D
But a house gets cold when you   cut the heating,
G   C(add9)
Without you to hold   I'll be freezing.
Em7
   Can't rely on my heart to beat in,
G   C(add9)
'Cause you take parts of it every evening.
Em7   D
Take words out of my mouth just from breathing,
G   C(add9)   G
Replace with phrases like "When you leaving me?"

Chorus 1

G   Am7   C   Em   G
Should I, should I? Maybe I'll get drunk a - gain.
     Em   G   Em   G   C   D
I'll be drunk a - gain, I'll be drunk a - gain to feel a little love.___

Verse 2

G
I wanna hold your heart in both hands,

                                        G/F♯   Em7
Not watch it fizzle at the bottom of a Coke can.

And I got no plans for the weekend,

So should we speak then, keep it between friends?

C(add9)   D   G
   Though I know you'll never love me like you used to.

There may be other people like us,

                               G/F♯
Who see the flicker a Clipper when they light up.

Em7   C(add9)
Flames just create us but burns don't heal like be - fore,

                               D   G
And you don't hold me any - more.____

Pre-chorus 2

          Em7   D
On cold days cold plays out like the band's name,

G   C(add9)
   I know I can't heal things with a handshake.

Em7   D
   You know I can change   as I began saying,

G   C(add9)
   You cut me wide open like landscape.

Em7   D
   Open bottles of beer but never champagne,

G   C(add9)
To applaud you with the sound that my hands make.

Chorus 2   As Chorus 1

Bridge

Em7   G
   All by my - self, I'm here again.

Em7   G
   All by my - self, you know I'll never change.

Em   G   C(add9)   Em
   All by my - self,   all by my - self.

Chorus 3

                     G   Em   G
I'm just drunk a - gain, I'll be   drunk a - gain,

             Em   G   C   D
I'll be   drunk a - gain to feel a little love.____

ENGLISH ROSE

Words & Music by Ed Sheeran & John McDaid

D5   Gadd9   Aadd4   Bm7   D/F#

⑥ = D   ③ = G
⑤ = A   ② = A
④ = D   ① = D

Intro | D5 | D5 |

Verse 1
          D5   Gadd9 D5   Gadd9   D5
          Across the sea   by the Tennessee skyline,
                  Gadd9   D5   Aadd4   D5
          They told me I'd find my hopes and my dreams.
                      Gadd9 D5   Gadd9   D5
          But I long to be   in the bed of my true love,
          Gadd9   D5   Aadd4 D5
          Back where I came from she's wait - ing for me.

Chorus 1
          (D5)   Gadd9 Aadd4   Bm7 Aadd4   Gadd9   D5
          So I'll make my   way through long winding country roads,
                      Gadd9 Aadd4 Bm7   Gadd9   Aadd4   D5
          But my heart   still   beats for my home and my English rose.

Verse 2
          (D5)   Gadd9 D5   Gadd9   D5
          I told my dad   on the phone it's amazing,
                      Gadd9   D5   Aadd4   D5
          From the straight to the crazy, these places I've seen.
                      Gadd9 D5   Gadd9   D5
          But I long to be   in the arms of my true love,
                  Gadd9   D5   Aadd4   D5
          Like he loves my mother, he understands me.

Chorus 2
          (D5) D/F#   Gadd9 Aadd4   Bm7 Aadd4   Gadd9   D5
          I'll spend my   days just traveling and playing shows,
                      Gadd9 Aadd4 Bm7   Gadd9   Aadd4   D5
          But my heart   still   beats for my home and my English rose.

‖: Gadd9 | Aadd9 | Bm7 | D5 |

| Gadd9 | Aadd9 | Bm7 | D5 :‖

D5   Gadd9 D5   Gadd9   D5

rse 3   I met a man   in a bar down in Memphis,

      Gadd9 D5   Aadd4   D5

He told me he went there to follow his dreams.

            Gadd9 D5   Gadd9   D5

And he told me, son,   you know, I lost my true love

      Gadd9   D5   Aadd4   D5

For the same exact reason that you crossed the sea.

D5 D/F♯ Gadd9 Aadd4 Bm7 Aadd4 Gadd9 D5

horus 3   And I   found truth in peo - ple I   barely know,

      Gadd9 Aadd4 Bm7   Gadd9   Aadd4 D5

But my heart   still   beats for my home and my English rose.

      Gadd9 Aadd4 Bm7   Gadd9   Aadd4 D5

Oh, my heart still   beats for my home and my English rose.

      Gadd9 Aadd4 Bm7   Gadd9   Aadd4 D5

Oh, my heart still   beats for my home and my English rose.

ERASER

Words & Music by Ed Sheeran & John McDaid

Em   C   Dadd4   G   D   Am   B7

Capo 4

Intro

‖: Em | Em | C | Dadd4   :‖

Verse 1

(Dadd4)   Em
I was born inside a small town, I lost that state of mind,
                                          C   Dad
Learned to sing inside the lord's house, but stopped at the age of nine
              Em
I forget when I get awards now, the wave I had to ride,
          C   Dadd4
The paving stones I played upon that kept me on the grind.
              Em
So blame it on the pain that blessed me with the life,
          C
Friends and family filled with envy,
                              Dadd4
    when they should be filled with pride.
                      Em
And when the world's against me is when I really come alive,
              C   Dadd4
And every day that Satan tempts me, I try to take it in my stride.
              Em
You know that I've got whisky with white lies and smoke in my lungs
      C   Dadd4
I think life has got to the point, I know without it's no fun.
          Em
I need to get in the right mind and clear myself up,
      C   Dadd4
Instead I look in the mirror, questioning what I've become.
              Em
Guess it's a stereotypical day for someone like me
          C   Dadd4
Without a nine to five job or a uni degree.
          Em
To be caught up in the trappings of the industry,
              C   Dadd4
Show me the locked doors, I'll find another use for the key

        and you'll see.

         C   **G**   **D**   **Am**

Pre-chorus 1   I'm well aware of certain things that can destroy a man like me,

    C   **G**   **D**   **B7**

        But with that said give me one more._____

     Em   **C**   **Dadd4**   **Em**

Chorus 1   Another one to take the sting away,

          C   **Dadd4**   **Em**

I am happy on my own so here I'll stay.

             C   **Dadd4**   **Em**

Save your loving arms for a rainy day,

                 C   **Dadd4 N.C.**

And I'll find comfort in my pain   eraser.

     (N.C.)   **Em**

Verse 2   I used to think that nothing could be better

                than touring the world with my songs,

             C   **Dadd4**

I chased the picture perfect life, I think they painted it wrong.

          Em

I think that money is the route of all evil and fame is hell,

    C   **Dadd4**

Relationships and hearts you fix, they break as well.

       Em

And ain't nobody want to see you down in the dumps,

            C   **Dadd4**

Because you're living your dream and it should be fun.

           Em

Please know that I'm not trying to preach like I'm reverend run,

      C   **Dadd4**

I beg you don't be disappointed with the man I've become.

        Em

Conversations with my father on the A14,

     C   **Dadd4**

Age twelve, telling me I've gotta chase those dreams.

          Em

Now, I'm playing for the people dad, and they know me,

      C   **Dadd4**

With my beaten small guitar, wearing the same old jeans.

         Em

Wembley stadium crowds, two hundred and forty thou',

                C   **Dadd4**

cont.   I may have grown up, but I hope that Damien's proud.

                       Em

And to the next generation, inspiration's allowed,

                  C   **Dadd4**   **N.C.**

The world may be filled with hate, but keep erasing it now, somehow.

          C   **G**   **D**   **Am**

Pre-chorus 2   I'm well aware of certain things that will befall a man like me,

          C   **G**   **D**   **B7**

But with that said give me one more.___

         Em   **C**   **Dadd4**   **Em**

Chorus 2   Another one to take the sting away,

               C   **Dadd4**   **Em**

Oh, I am happy on my own so here I'll stay.

                   C   **Dadd4**   **Em**

Well, save your loving arms for a rainy day,

                 C   **Dadd4**

And I'll find comfort in my pain eraser.

Em   **C**   **Dadd4**

And I'll find comfort in my pain eraser.

Em   **C**   **Dadd4** **N.C.**

And I'll find comfort in my pain   eraser.

         Em

Bridge   Welcome to the new show,

         C   **Dadd4**

I guess you know I've been away.

         Em

Where I'm heading who knows,

         C   **Dadd4**

But my heart will stay the same.

         Em

Welcome to the new show,

         C   **Dadd4**

I guess you know I've been away.

         Em

Where I'm heading who knows,

         C N.C.

My pain eraser.

Em   C   Dadd4
And I'll find comfort in my pain eraser.

Em   C   Dadd4
And I'll find comfort in my pain eraser.

Em   C   Dadd4
And I'll find comfort in my pain eraser.

Em   C   Dadd4 N.C.
And I'll find comfort in my pain   eraser.

EVEN MY DAD DOES SOMETIMES

Words & Music by Ed Sheeran & Amy Wadge

Intro | D | A G | D | A G ‖

Verse 1
D   A   G   D   A G
It's all right to cry,   even my dad does some - times,
D   A   G   D   A G
So don't wipe your eyes,   tears re - mind you you're a - live.
D   A   G   D   A
It's all right to die 'cause death's the only thing you haven't tried,
D   A G   D A G
But just for tonight   hold on.

Chorus 1
D/F♯   G
So live life like you're giving up
D/F♯   G
'Cause you act like you are.
D/F♯   G
Go ahead and just live it up,
Bm   A   G
Go on and tear me apart.

Verse 2
D   A   G   D   A G
It's all right to shake,   even my hand does some - times,
D   A   G   D   A G
So inside we rage   against the dying of the light.
D   A   G   D   A G
It's all right to say that death's the only thing you haven't tried,
D   A G   D A G
But just for today___ hold on.___

D/F♯   **G**
So live life like you're giving up

D/F♯   **G**
'Cause you act like you are.

D/F♯   **G**
Go ahead and just live it up,

Bm   **A**   **G**
Go on and tear me apart, hold on.

Instrumental ‖: **D** | **G** | **D/F♯** | **G** :‖ *Play 4 times*

Chorus 3

D/F♯   **G**
Live life like you're giving up

D/F♯   **G**
'Cause you act like you are.

D/F♯   **G**
Go ahead and just live it up,

Bm   **A**   **G**
Go on and tear me apart and hold on.

DON'T

Words & Music by Ed Sheeran, Ali Jones-Muhammad,
Raphael Saadiq, Benjamin Levin, Conesha Owens & Dawn Robinson

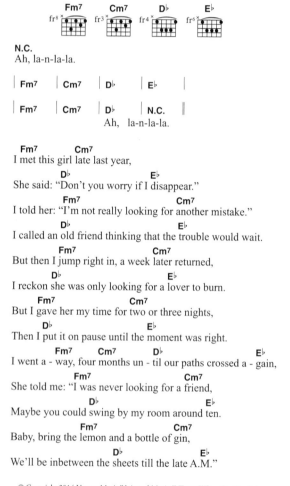

Intro

N.C.
Ah, la-n-la-la.

| Fm7 | Cm7 | D♭ | E♭ | |

| Fm7 | Cm7 | D♭ | N.C. ‖
               Ah, la-n-la-la.

Verse 1

     Fm7   Cm7
I met this girl late last year,
            D♭   E♭
She said: "Don't you worry if I disappear."
           Fm7   Cm7
I told her: "I'm not really looking for another mistake."
        D♭   E♭
I called an old friend thinking that the trouble would wait.
          Fm7   Cm7
But then I jump right in, a week later returned,
        D♭   E♭
I reckon she was only looking for a lover to burn.
     Fm7   Cm7
But I gave her my time for two or three nights,
        D♭   E♭
Then I put it on pause until the moment was right.
       Fm7   Cm7   D♭   E♭
I went a - way, four months un - til our paths crossed a - gain,
         Fm7   Cm7
She told me: "I was never looking for a friend,
          D♭   E♭
Maybe you could swing by my room around ten.
          Fm7   Cm7
Baby, bring the lemon and a bottle of gin,
             D♭   E♭
We'll be inbetween the sheets till the late A.M."

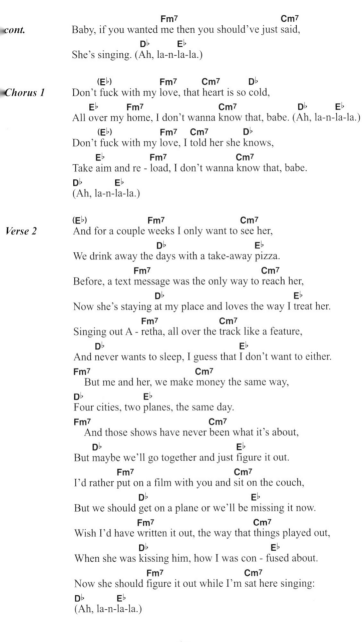

                           Fm7   Cm7

cont.   Baby, if you wanted me then you should've just said,

                      Db   Eb

          She's singing. (Ah, la-n-la-la.)

                 (Eb)   Fm7   Cm7   Db

Chorus 1   Don't fuck with my love, that heart is so cold,

             Eb   Fm7   Cm7   Db   Eb

          All over my home, I don't wanna know that, babe. (Ah, la-n-la-la.)

                 (Eb)   Fm7   Cm7   Db

          Don't fuck with my love, I told her she knows,

               Eb   Fm7   Cm7

          Take aim and re - load, I don't wanna know that, babe.

          Db   Eb

          (Ah, la-n-la-la.)

          (Eb)   Fm7   Cm7

Verse 2   And for a couple weeks I only want to see her,

                            Db   Eb

          We drink away the days with a take-away pizza.

                  Fm7   Cm7

          Before, a text message was the only way to reach her,

                       Db   Eb

          Now she's staying at my place and loves the way I treat her.

                  Fm7   Cm7

          Singing out A - retha, all over the track like a feature,

               Db   Eb

          And never wants to sleep, I guess that I don't want to either.

          Fm7   Cm7

            But me and her, we make money the same way,

          Db   Eb

          Four cities, two planes, the same day.

          Fm7   Cm7

           And those shows have never been what it's about,

            Db   Eb

          But maybe we'll go together and just figure it out.

                 Fm7   Cm7

          I'd rather put on a film with you and sit on the couch,

                    Db   Eb

          But we should get on a plane or we'll be missing it now.

                  Fm7   Cm7

          Wish I'd have written it out, the way that things played out,

                  Db   Eb

          When she was kissing him, how I was con - fused about.

                 Fm7   Cm7

          Now she should figure it out while I'm sat here singing:

          Db   Eb

          (Ah, la-n-la-la.)

Chorus 2   As Chorus 1

                Fm⁷   Cm⁷

Verse 3   (Knock, knock, knock) On my hotel door

        D♭   E♭

I don't even know if she knows what for.

            Fm⁷   Cm⁷

She was crying on my shoulder, I already told ya,

        D♭   E♭

Trust and respect is what we do this for.

        Fm⁷   Cm⁷

I never intended to be next,

          D♭   E♭

But you didn't need to take him to bed, that's all.

        Fm⁷   Cm⁷

And I never saw him as a threat,

            D♭   E♭

Until you disappeared with him to have sex, of course.

        Fm⁷   Cm⁷

  It's not like we were both on tour,

          D♭   E♭

We were staying on the same hotel floor.

         Fm⁷   Cm⁷

And I wasn't looking for a promise or com - mitment,

         D♭   E♭

It was never just fun and I thought you were different.

        Fm⁷   Cm⁷

This is not the way you rea - lise what you wanted,

          D♭   E♭

It's a bit too much, too late if I'm honest.

         Fm⁷   Cm⁷

And all this time God knows I'm singing:

        D♭   E♭

(Ah, la-n-la-la.)

Chorus 3   As Chorus 1

             (E♭)   Fm⁷   Cm⁷   D♭

Chorus 4   Don't fuck with my love, that heart is so cold,

         E♭   Fm⁷   Cm⁷   D♭   E♭

All over my home, I don't wanna know that, babe. (Ah, la-n-la-la.)

        (E♭)   Fm⁷ Cm⁷   D♭

Don't fuck with my love, I told her she knows,

        E♭   Fm⁷   Cm⁷   N.C.

Take aim and re - load, I don't wanna know that, babe.(Ah, la-n-la-la.)

50

EVERYTHING HAS CHANGED

Words & Music by Ed Sheeran & Taylor Swift

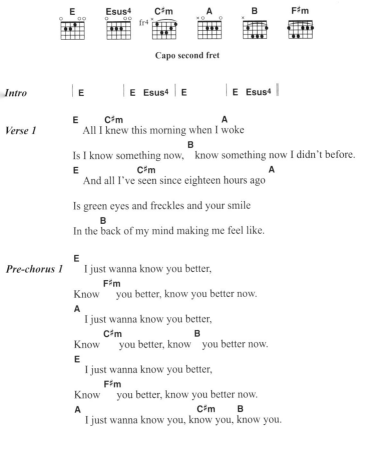

Capo second fret

Intro　　　| E　　　| E Esus⁴ | E　　　| E Esus⁴ ‖

Verse 1
```
        E   C#m                    A
    All I knew this morning when I woke
                        B
    Is I know something now,   know something now I didn't before.
        E        C#m                    A
        And all I've seen since eighteen hours ago

    Is green eyes and freckles and your smile
                B
    In the back of my mind making me feel like.
```

Pre-chorus 1
```
        E
        I just wanna know you better,
                F#m
    Know     you better, know you better now.
        A
        I just wanna know you better,
            C#m            B
    Know     you better, know     you better now.
        E
        I just wanna know you better,
                F#m
    Know     you better, know you better now.
        A                    C#m        B
        I just wanna know you, know you, know you.
```

Chorus 1

(B)   E
'Cause all I know is we said hello

C♯m
And your eyes look like coming home,

B   A
All I know is a simple name,   everything has changed.

E   C♯m
All I know is you held the door, you'll be mine and I'll be yours,

B   A
All I know since yesterday is everything has changed.

Link | E | E Esus4 | E | E Esus4 ‖

Verse 2

E   C♯m   A
And all my walls stood tall painted blue,

B
And I'll take 'em down, take 'em down and open up the door for yo

E   C♯m   A
And all I feel in my stomach is butterflies,

The beautiful kind, making up for lost time,

B
Taking flight, making me feel right like.

Pre-chorus 2   As Pre-chorus 1

Chorus 2   As Chorus 1

Bridge

C♯m   A
Come back and tell me why,

E   B
I'm feeling like I've missed you all this time.____

C♯m   A
And meet me there to - night

E   B
And let me know that it's not all in my mind.

E
I just wanna know you better,

F♯m
Know   you better, know you better now.

A   **C♯m**   **B**
I just wanna know you, know you, know you.

Chorus 3   As Chorus 1

Chorus 4

E   **C♯m**
All I know is we said, hello,   so dust off your highest hopes,

B   **A**
All I know is pouring rain   and everything has changed.

E   **C♯m**
All I know is a new found grace, all my days I'll know your face,

B   **A**   **N.C.**
All I know since yesterday   is   everything has changed.

FALL

Words & Music by Ed Sheeran & Amy Wadge

E Esus⁴ Aadd⁹ C♯m⁷ Badd⁴ Asus²

Intro ‖: E | E | E | E Esus⁴ :‖

Verse 1

  E
  You and I, two of a mind,
  Aadd⁹
   This love's one of a kind.
  E   C♯m⁷
  You and I, we're drifting ___
  Aadd⁹   E
   Over the edge.

Chorus 1

  (E) Aadd⁹ Badd⁴
  And I will fall for you,
       E
  And I will fall for you.
   Aadd⁹   Badd⁴
  If I fall for you,
      E
  Would you fall too?

Verse 2

  (E)
  You and I, learning to speak
  Aadd⁹
   With kisses on cheeks.
  E   C♯m⁷
  You and I, we're lifted___
  Aadd⁹   E
   Over the edge.___

Chorus 2 as Chorus 1

(E)   **Aadd⁹**   **Badd⁴**
And I will fall for you,

              E
And I will fall for you.

     Aadd⁹   **Badd⁴**
If I   fall for you,

             E
Would you fall too?

          Asus² **E**
Would you fall   too?

          Asus² **E**
Would you fall   too?

          Asus² **E**
Would you fall   too?

          Asus² **E**
Would you fall   too?

FIRE ALARMS

Words & Music by Ed Sheeran & Amy Wadge

C   C/B   C/B♭   Am⁷   Fmaj⁷   G/B   G

Capo 3

Intro   ‖: C | C/B | C/B♭ | Am⁷ C/B :‖

Verse 1
C   C/B C/B♭   Am⁷   C/B C   C/B C/B♭ Am⁷
The rain wont stop falling, it's harder than be - fore,
C/B C   C/B   C/B♭   Am⁷   C C/B C/B♭ Am⁷
This car keeps on stalling, pedal to the floor.

Chorus 1
Fmaj⁷   C   G/B
    And what I need to know is if you love me and I
Fmaj⁷   C   G/B
    Really need to know is if you want me when you
Fmaj⁷   C G/B   Fmaj⁷   C   G/B
    Call,_____ if you want me when you   call?_____

Verse 2
C   C/B   C/B♭
    We were young and we were foolish,
Am⁷   C   C/B C/B♭ Am⁷
    School books in our arms,
C   C/B   C/B♭
    Dodging homework, dodging classes
Am⁷   C   C/B C/B♭ Am⁷
    To set off fire alarms.

Chorus 2
Fmaj⁷   C   G/B   G
    And what I need to know is if you love me and I
Fmaj⁷   C   G/B   G
    Really need to know is if you need me when you
Fmaj⁷   C G/B   G   Fmaj⁷   C G/B G
    Call, _____ if you want me when you   call?_____

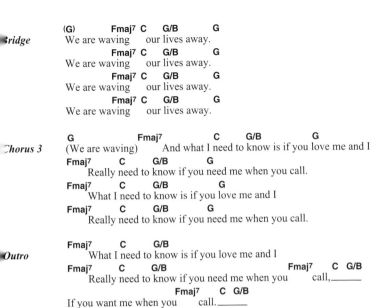

Bridge

(G) **Fmaj7 C G/B** **G**
We are waving our lives away.

    Fmaj7 C G/B **G**
We are waving our lives away.

    Fmaj7 C G/B **G**
We are waving our lives away.

    Fmaj7 C G/B **G**
We are waving our lives away.

Chorus 3

G   **Fmaj7**   **C** **G/B**   **G**
(We are waving) And what I need to know is if you love me and I

Fmaj7 **C** **G/B** **G**
  Really need to know if you need me when you call.

Fmaj7 **C** **G/B** **G**
  What I need to know is if you love me and I

Fmaj7 **C** **G/B** **G**
  Really need to know if you need me when you call.

Outro

Fmaj7 **C** **G/B**
  What I need to know is if you love me and I

Fmaj7 **C** **G/B**   **Fmaj7** **C G/B**
  Really need to know if you need me when you call,_____

       Fmaj7 **C G/B**
If you want me when you call._____

EVERYTHING YOU ARE

Words & Music by Ed Sheeran

C Cadd9 Cadd9/B Am7 F%

G D5 F Em Am

Capo 7

Intro | C | Cadd9 | C | Cadd9 |

| C | Cadd9 | C | Cadd9/B |

Verse 1
Am7   F%   C   G   Am7
    I didn't mean to break your heart, I was just lonely,
                  F%   C   G
And everybody falls apart sometimes.
Am7   F%
    I know you've found another one,
C   G   Am7   F%   C   G
    But won't you just hold me tonight?

Verse 2
Am7   F%   C   G   Am7
    I wish I never called you up,   nobody told me,
                    F%   C   G
And they don't know we don't speak anymore.
Am7   F%
    So take a good look at us,
C   G   Am7   F%   C
    Won't you just hold me tonight?

Pre-chorus 1
G   D5   F
    And I will stop trying to fall in love again,
                       C   Em
And keep it a secret,   it never works out, anyway.
            D5   F
But I am not, anything like I was,
                      C   Em
'Cause you were the only one for me.

© Copyright 2014 Sony/ATV Music Publishing.
All Rights Reserved. International Copyright Secured.

58

Chorus 1

F C G
'Cause maybe I don't wanna lose a lover and friend
Am
In one night, if that's alright,
G C
I shouldn't have fucked with your mind
F C
And your life too many times.
F C
Or maybe I don't wanna be lonely,
G Am D5
Darling, you are my only love,
F
Behind my truth lies everything you want.

Link 1 | C | Cadd9 | C | G |

Verse 3

Am7 F6/9 C G Am7
I never meant to sleep around, I was just lonely,
F6/9 C G N.C.
You did the same, again and again and again, whoa, I know.
Am7 F6/9
So here's to the both of us,
C G Am7 F6/9 C
Here's to our story tonight.

Pre-chorus 2 as Pre-chorus 1

Chorus 2 as Chorus 1

Link 2 | C | Cadd9 | C | C |

    (C)   **D5**   **F**
When I see my future it is with you,
   C   **Em**
   And we'll get there.
       D5   **F**   **C**
And I want my children to be with you,
            Em
And we'll get there.

Chorus 3

   F   **C**   **G**
   'Cause maybe I don't wanna lose a lover and friend
        Am
In one night, if that's alright,
 G   **C**
   I shouldn't have fucked with your mind
 F   **C**
And your life too many times.
 F   **C**
   Or maybe I don't wanna be lonely,
 G   **Am**   **D5**
   Darling, you are my only love,
          F   **D5**
Behind my truth lies everything you want.
          F   **D5**
Behind my truth lies everything you want.
          F   **C**
Behind my truth lies everything you are.

FIREFLY

Words & Music by Ed Sheeran

E5   B7/A   C#m   A   B

Intro | E5 | E5   B7/A | C#m | C#m   A |

               | E5 | E5   A | E5 | E5 |

Verse 1
E5   B7/A   C#m
I fell in love next to ___ you,
A   E5   B7/A   C#m
Burning fires in this room.
A   E5   B7/A   C#m
It just fits, light and smooth,
A   E5   B   E5
Like my feet in my shoes.
                 B7/A   C#m
Little one, lie with me,
A   E5   B7/A   C#m
Sew your heart to my sleeve.
A   E5   B7/A   C#m
We'll stay quiet under - neath
A   E5   B   E5
Shooting stars if it helps you sleep

Pre-chorus 1
          A   C#m
And hold me tight, don't let me breathe,
A   B
Feeling like you won't believe.

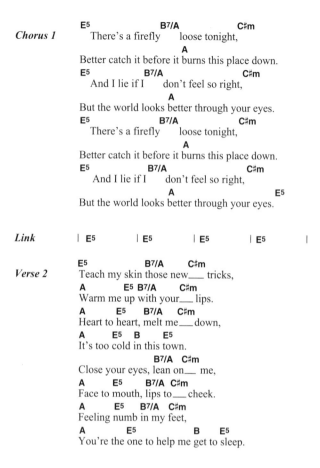

Chorus 1

E5   B7/A   C#m
There's a firefly   loose tonight,
                       A
Better catch it before it burns this place down.
E5   B7/A   C#m
And I lie if I   don't feel so right,
                    A
But the world looks better through your eyes.
E5   B7/A   C#m
There's a firefly   loose tonight,
                       A
Better catch it before it burns this place down.
E5   B7/A   C#m
And I lie if I   don't feel so right,
                    A   E5
But the world looks better through your eyes.

Link

| E5 | E5 | E5 | E5 |

Verse 2

E5   B7/A   C#m
Teach my skin those new___ tricks,
A   E5 B7/A   C#m
Warm me up with your___ lips.
A   E5   B7/A   C#m
Heart to heart, melt me___down,
A   E5   B   E5
It's too cold in this town.
                      B7/A C#m
Close your eyes, lean on___ me,
A   E5   B7/A C#m
Face to mouth, lips to___ cheek.
A   E5   B7/A C#m
Feeling numb in my feet,
A   E5   B   E5
You're the one to help me get to sleep.

Pre chorus 2 as Pre-chorus 1

Chorus 2 as Chorus 1

Bridge	**A**

Bridge

        A
It's only been one night of love
      C♯m
And maybe that is not enough.
A
Hold me tight, don't let me breathe,
C♯m
Feeling like you won't believe.
        A
It's only been one night of love
      C♯m
And maybe that is not enough.
A
Hold me tight, don't let me breathe,
B
Feeling like you won't believe.

Chorus 3 as Chorus 1

FRIENDS

Words & Music by Ed Sheeran

A   E   B   C#m   F#m

Verse 1

N.C.   A   E
We're not, no we're not friends,   nor have we ever been,
              B   C#m
We just try to keep those secrets in a lie.
            A   E
And if they find out, will it all go wrong?
                B   A E
And heaven knows, no one wants it to.

Pre-chorus 1

(E)   C#m
So I could take the back road,
                            A   B
But your eyes will lead me straight back home.
                  A   E
And if you know me like I know you,
                  B
You should love me, you should know.

Chorus 1

E   F#m
Friends just sleep in another bed,
          A   B   E
And friends don't treat me like you do.
          C#m   A   E
Well, I know that there's a limit to everything,
          A   B   E
But my friends won't love me like you.
          A   B   E
No, my friends won't love me like you.

Verse 2

N.C.   A   E
We're not friends, we could be anything,
        B   C#m
If we try to keep those secrets safe.
                A   E
No one will find out if it all went wrong,
                B   A   E
They'll never know what we've been through.

Bridge

    (E)   **A**
But then again, if we're not friends,
          C♯m   **B**
Someone else might love you too.
         A
And then again, if we're not friends,
           C♯m   **B**
There'd be nothing I could do.

Chorus 3

  N.C.   **E**   **F♯m**
And that's why friends should sleep in other beds,
      A   **B**   **E**
And friends shouldn't kiss me like you do.
      C♯m   **A**   **E**
And I know that there's a limit to everything,
    A   **B**   **E**
But my friends won't love me like you.
    A   **B**   **E**
No, my friends won't love me like you do.
    A   **B**   **E**
Oh, my friends will never love me like you.

GALWAY GIRL

Words & Music by Ed Sheeran, John McDaid,
Foy Vance, Amy Wadge, Damien McKee, Eamon Murray,
Niamh Dunne, Liam Bradley & Sean Graham

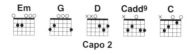

Capo 2

Pre-chorus 1
        Em   **G**
She played the fiddle in an Irish band,
          D   **Cadd9**
But she fell in love with an English man.
                   G
Kissed her on the neck and then I took her by the hand,
 D
Said, baby, I just want to dance.

Verse 1
        N.C   **Em**   **G**
I met her on Grafton street right outside of the bar,
             D   **C**
She shared a cigarette with me while her brother played the guitar.
             Em   **G**
She asked me what does it mean the Gaelic ink on your arm?
          D   **N.C.**
Said it was one of my friend's songs. Do you want to drink on?
G   **Em**   **G**
She took Jamie as a chaser, Jack for the fun,
         D   **C**
She got Arthur on the table, with Johnny riding as shot gun.
Am   **G**
Chatted some more, one more drink at the bar,
          D
Then put Van on the jukebox, got up to dance, you know.

Pre-chorus 2 as Pre-chorus 1

Chorus 1
        N.C.   **C**   **G**   **D**   **Em**
With my pretty little Galway Girl.
                         C   **G**   **D**   **Em**
You're my pretty little Galway Girl.

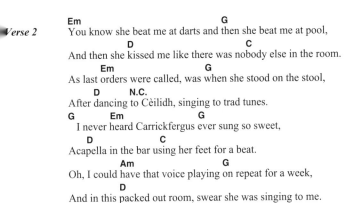

Verse 2

Em   G
You know she beat me at darts and then she beat me at pool,
                 D   C
And then she kissed me like there was nobody else in the room.
       Em   G
As last orders were called, was when she stood on the stool,
      D   N.C.
After dancing to Cèilidh, singing to trad tunes.
G   Em   G
  I never heard Carrickfergus ever sung so sweet,
      D   C
Acapella in the bar using her feet for a beat.
           Am   G
Oh, I could have that voice playing on repeat for a week,
           D
And in this packed out room, swear she was singing to me.

Pre-chorus 3 as Pre-chorus 1

                N.C.   C   G
Chorus 2   My pretty little Galway girl.
                D   Em   C   G
  My, my, my, my, my, my, my Galway girl.
                D   Em   C   G
  My, my, my, my, my, my, my Galway girl.
                D   Em   C   G   D   Em
  My, my, my, my, my, my, my Galway girl.

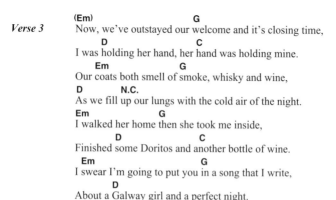

Verse 3

   (Em)   **G**
Now, we've outstayed our welcome and it's closing time,
      D   **C**
I was holding her hand, her hand was holding mine.
       Em   **G**
Our coats both smell of smoke, whisky and wine,
D   **N.C.**
As we fill up our lungs with the cold air of the night.
Em   **G**
I walked her home then she took me inside,
       D   **C**
Finished some Doritos and another bottle of wine.
  Em   **G**
I swear I'm going to put you in a song that I write,
       D
About a Galway girl and a perfect night.

Pre-chorus 4 as Pre-chorus 1

Chorus 3 as Chorus 2

      | **C G** | **D Em** | **C G** | **D Em** |

      | **C G** | **D Em** | **C G** | **D Em** ‖

GIVE ME LOVE

Words & Music by Ed Sheeran, Christopher Leonard & Jake Gosling

| Am | F | C | Dm | G/B | G | Fmaj7 |

Capo first fret

Intro   ‖: Am | F | C | C :‖   *Play 4 times*

Verse 1

Am   F   C
Give me love   like her,

Am   F   C
  'Cause lately I've been waking up alone.

Am   F   C
  Paint splattered teardrops on my shirt,

Am   F   C
  Told you I'd let them go.

Pre-chorus 1

(C)   Dm
And that I'll fight my corner,

             F
Maybe to - night I'll call ya

       C   G/B G
After my blood turns into alcohol,

   Dm   F
No, I just wanna hold ya.

Chorus 1

C   Dm   Fmaj7
  Give a little time to me or burn this out,

C   Dm   Fmaj7
  We'll play hide and seek to turn this around,

C   Dm   Fmaj7
  All I want is the taste that your lips allow.

cont.

Am   G   Fmaj7
My, my,   my, my,____ oh give me love.

(Am)   (F)   (C)
My, my,   my, my,____ oh give me love.

(Am)   (F)   (C)
My, my,   my, my,____ oh give me love.

(Am)   (F)   (C)
My, my,   my, my,____ oh give me love.

(Am)   (F)   (C)
My, my,   my, my,____ give me love.

Verse 2

Am   F   C
Give me love like never before,

Am   F   C
'Cause lately I've been craving more.

Am   F   C
And it's been a while but   I still feel the same,

Am   F   C
Maybe I should let you go.

Pre-chorus 2

(C)   Dm
You know I'll fight my corner

                   F
And that to - night I'll call ya

            C   G/B G
After my blood is drowning in alcohol,

   Dm   F
No, I just wanna hold ya.

Chorus 2

C   Dm   Fmaj7
Give a little time to me or burn this out,

C   Dm   Fmaj7
We'll play hide and seek to turn this around,

C   Dm   Fmaj7
All I want is the taste that your lips allow.

Am   G   Fmaj7
My, my,   my, my,____ oh give me love.

C   D   Fmaj7
Give a little time to me or burn this out,

C   D   Fmaj7
We'll play hide and seek to turn this around,

C   D   Fmaj7
All I want is the taste that your lips allow.

Am   **G**   **Fmaj7**
My, my,   my, my,___ oh give me love.

Am   **F**   **C**
My, my,   my, my,___ oh give me love.

Am   **F**   **C**
My, my,   my, my,___ oh give me love.

Am   **F**   **C**
My, my,   my, my,___ oh give me love.

Am   **F**   **C**
My, my,   my, my,___ oh give me love.

Bridge

     Am   **G**   **Am**
‖: M-my my, m-my my, m-my my, give me love, lov - er.

                        G   **Am**
M-my my, m-my my, m-my my, give me love, lov - er.

                        G   **Am**
M-my my, m-my my, m-my my, give me love, lov - er.

                        G   **Am**
M-my my, m-my my, m-my my, give me love, lov - er. :‖ *Play 4 times*

Outro

     Am   **F**
‖:   My, my, my, my,___ oh give me love.

C
My, my, my, my, oh give me love.

Am   **F**
My, my, my, my,___ oh give me love.

C
My, my, my, my, oh give me love. :‖ *Play 3 times*

GOLD RUSH

Words & Music by Ed Sheeran & Amy Wadge

E   F♯m   A   C♯m   B

Intro

| E | F♯m | A | A | |

| E | F♯m | A | A | |

Verse 1

E   F♯m   A
Smoke   alarm went off at nine,

E   F♯m   A
I woke up, wiped the sleep out of my eye.

E   F♯m   A
She left a note,   I'll be back in five,

E   F♯m   A
Well, I'm still waiting for that moment to arrive, hey.

Pre-chorus 1

C♯m   A   B
I was told to put my job in front of you,

C♯m   A   B
But it won't hold me like you do.

Chorus 1

N.C.   E   F♯m
But I do it for the love, waiting on the gold rush,

              A
Keep it on the edge, smoking on a roll up.

               E   F♯m
When I see my friends, all they say is hold up

         A
And re - member the time

              E   F♯m
When we were in school listening to grown-ups.

         A
Didn't learn a thing but then again, you know what,

             E   F♯m   A
You know how to sing, but you don't know anything other than that.

cont.

N.C.   E
So maybe you should learn to love her

F#m   A
  Like, like the way.

                          E
Maybe you should learn to love her

F#m   A
  Like, like the way.

                           E
And maybe you should learn to love her

F#m   A
  Like, like the way.

                           E
And maybe you should learn to love her

F#m   A   N.C.
  Like, like the way you wanna be loved.

Verse 2

E   F#m   A
I never told her that I liked

E   F#m   A
The way she dances slightly out of time

E   F#m   A   E
And pre - tends she knows the words to a song she's never heard

         F#m   A
But I tell her all the time, hey.

Pre-chorus 2   As Pre-chorus 1

Chorus 2   As Chorus 1

Instrumental ‖: E | F#m | A | A   :‖ *Play 4 times*

Chorus 3   As Chorus 1

GRADE 8

Words & Music by Ed Sheeran, Robert Conlon & Sukhdeep Uppal

Gm   B♭   E♭   D   D7

Verse 1

Gm   B♭   E♭   D
   My mind is a warrior,   my heart is a foreig - ner,

Gm   B♭   E♭   D
   My eyes are the colour of red like a sun - set.

Gm   B♭   E♭   D
   I'll never keep it bottled up   and left to the hands of the co - roner,

Gm   B♭   E♭   D
   Be a true heart not a follower,   we're not done yet.

Pre-chorus 1

Gm   B♭   E♭
   And I see it in your movements tonight,

                        D
If we should ever do this right,

Gm   B♭   E♭   D
   I'm never gonna let you down,   oh, I'll never let you down.

Gm   B♭   E♭
   And I'm keeping on the down low

                        D
And I'll keep you around so I'll know

Gm   B♭   E♭   D
   That I'll never let you down,   I'll never let you down.

Chorus 1

(D)   Gm   B♭
You're strumming on my heart strings like you were a grade eight,

E♭
But I've never felt this way.

        D7   Gm   B♭   E♭
I'll pick your feet up off of the ground and never ever let you down.

D7   Gm   B♭
Now, you're strumming on my heart strings like you were a grade eigh

E♭
But I've never felt this way,

        D7   Gm   B♭   E♭   D7
I'll pick your feet up off of the ground and never ever let you down.

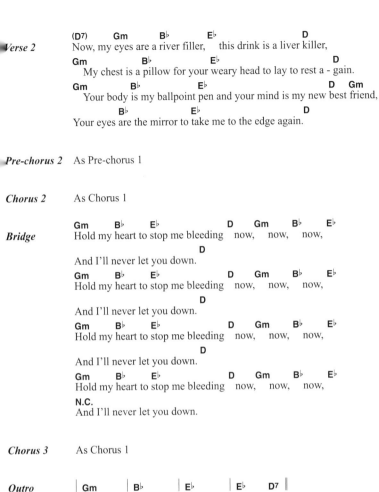

Verse 2

(D7)   Gm   B♭   E♭   D
Now, my eyes are a river filler,   this drink is a liver killer,

Gm   B♭   E♭   D
My chest is a pillow for your weary head to lay to rest a - gain.

Gm   B♭   E♭   D   Gm
Your body is my ballpoint pen and your mind is my new best friend,

           B♭   E♭   D
Your eyes are the mirror to take me to the edge again.

Pre-chorus 2   As Pre-chorus 1

Chorus 2   As Chorus 1

Bridge

Gm   B♭   E♭   D   Gm   B♭   E♭
Hold my heart to stop me bleeding now,   now,   now,

                                       D
And I'll never let you down.

Gm   B♭   E♭   D   Gm   B♭   E♭
Hold my heart to stop me bleeding now,   now,   now,

                                       D
And I'll never let you down.

Gm   B♭   E♭   D   Gm   B♭   E♭
Hold my heart to stop me bleeding now,   now,   now,

                                       D
And I'll never let you down.

Gm   B♭   E♭   D   Gm   B♭   E♭
Hold my heart to stop me bleeding now,   now,   now,

N.C.
And I'll never let you down.

Chorus 3   As Chorus 1

Outro | Gm | B♭ | E♭ | E♭   D7 ‖

HAPPIER

Words & Music by Ed Sheeran, Ryan Tedder & Benjamin Levin

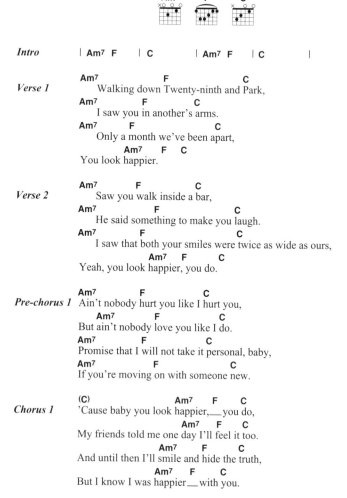

Intro | Am⁷ F | C | Am⁷ F | C |

Verse 1
Am⁷   F   C
    Walking down Twenty-ninth and Park,
Am⁷   F   C
    I saw you in another's arms.
Am⁷   F   C
    Only a month we've been apart,
        Am⁷   F   C
You look happier.

Verse 2
Am⁷   F   C
    Saw you walk inside a bar,
Am⁷   F   C
    He said something to make you laugh.
Am⁷   F   C
    I saw that both your smiles were twice as wide as ours,
       Am⁷   F   C
Yeah, you look happier, you do.

Pre-chorus 1
Am⁷   F   C
Ain't nobody hurt you like I hurt you,
   Am⁷   F   C
But ain't nobody love you like I do.
Am⁷   F   C
Promise that I will not take it personal, baby,
Am⁷   F   C
If you're moving on with someone new.

Chorus 1
(C)   Am⁷   F   C
'Cause baby you look happier,__ you do,
          Am⁷   F   C
My friends told me one day I'll feel it too.
       Am⁷   F   C
And until then I'll smile and hide the truth,
       Am⁷   F   C
But I know I was happier __ with you.

Link 1

    (C)   Am7
Hey yeah, hey yeah, hey yeah.

Verse 3

    (Am7)   F   C
Sat in the corner of the room,
Am7   F   C
Everything's reminding me of you.
Am7   F   C
Nursing an empty bottle
                           Am7   F   C
And telling myself you're happier,— aren't you?

Pre-chorus 2

Am7   F   C
Ain't nobody hurt you like I hurt you,
      Am7   F   C
But ain't nobody need you like I do.
Am7   F   C
I know that there's others that deserve you,
          Am7   F   C
But my darling I am still in love with you.

Chorus 2

    (C)   Am7   F   C
But I guess you look happier,— you do,
                      Am7   F   C
My friends told me one day I'll feel it too.
           Am7   F   C
I could try to smile and hide the truth,
             Am7   F   C
But I know I was happier— with you.

Link 2

    (C)   Am7 F C
Hey yeah, hey yeah, hey yeah.
                        Am7 F C
Hey yeah, hey yeah, hey yeah.
                        Am7 F C
Hey yeah, hey yeah, hey yeah.—
                        Am7 F C
Hey yeah, hey yeah, hey yeah.

Chorus 3

(C)   Am7   F   C
'Cause baby, you look happier,__ you do,

                         Am7   F   C
I knew one day you'd fall for someone new.

                       Am7   F   C
But if he breaks your heart like lovers do,

                        Am7   F   C
Just know that I'll be waiting here__ for you.

HEARTS DON'T BREAK AROUND HERE

Words & Music by Ed Sheeran & John McDaid

Capo 7

Verse 1

   C   G   Am7
    She is the sweetest thing that I know,
                             F   C
You should see the way she holds me when the lights go low,
                         G   Am7   F   C
Shakes my soul like a pot hole,   every time.
                       G   Am7
I took my heart upon a one way trip,
                     F   C
Guess she went wandering off with it.
                    G   Am7
Unlike most women I know,
                       F
This one will bring it back whole.
          C   G   Am7
Daisies, daisies perched upon your forehead,
G   F   C   G
Oh my baby, lately I know.

Chorus 1

N.C.   C   G   Am7
That every night I'll kiss you you'll say in my ear,
                  F   G   C
Oh, we're in love aren't we?
                     G   Am7   F   G C
Hands in your hair,   fingers and thumbs, baby.
                        G   Am7
I feel safe when you're holding me near,
               F   G   C
Love the way that you conquer your fear.
          Am7   G   F
You know hearts don't break around here.
                  C   G   Am7
Oh yeah, yeah, yeah,
F   (C)
Yeah, yeah, yeah, yeah.

Verse 2

     C   **G**   **Am7**
     She is the river flow in Orwell,
                  F
And tin wind chimes used for doorbells,
     C   **G**   **Am7**   **F**
     Fields and trees and her smell   fill my lungs.
     C   **G**   **Am7**
     Spent my summer time beside her
                       F
And the rest of the year the same.
     C   **G**   **Am7**
     She is the flint that sparks the lighter,
                   F
And the fuel that will hold the flame.
          C   **G**   **Am7**
Oh roses, roses laid upon your bedspread,
G   **F**   **C**   **G**
Oh my, hold this, oh this, I know.

Chorus 2

N.C.   **C**   **G**   **Am7**
That every night I'll kiss you you'll say in my ear
              F   **G**   **C**
Oh we're in love aren't we?
             G   **Am7**   **F**   **G C**
Hands in your hair,   fingers and thumbs, baby.
                 G   **Am7**
I feel safe when you're holding me near,
        F   **C**
Love the way that you conquer your fear.
       Am7   **G**   **F**
You know hearts don't break around here,

Oh yeah, yeah, yeah.

Bridge

(F)   C   G   Am⁷   G   F
Well I found love in the inside the arms of a woman I know,

             C   G   Am⁷ G   F
She is the lighthouse in the night that will safely guide me home.

          C   G   Am⁷   G   F
And I'm not scared of passing over or the thought of growing old,

                  G
Because from now until I go

Chorus 3

(G)   C   G   Am⁷
Every night I'll kiss you you'll say in my ear,

             F   G   C
Oh, we're in love aren't we?

         G   Am⁷   F   G C
Hands in your hair,   fingers and thumbs, baby.

                G   Am⁷
I feel safe when you're holding me near,

      F   C
Love the way that you conquer your fear.

      Am⁷   G   F
You know hearts don't break around here.

Oh yeah, yeah.

Chorus 4

(F)   C   G   Am⁷
Every night I'll kiss you you'll say in my ear,

             F   G   C
Oh we're in love aren't we?

         G   Am⁷   F   G C
Hands in your hair,   fingers and thumbs, baby.

                G   Am⁷
I feel safe when you're holding me near.

      F   C
Love the way that you conquer your fear,

      Am⁷   G   F
You know hearts don't break around here.

             Am⁷
Yeah, yeah, yeah.

             G   F
You know hearts don't break around here.

                  C
Oh yeah, yeah, yeah, yeah.

HOMELESS

Words & Music by Ed Sheeran & Anna Krantz

E	A	F#m	D

Intro
   E   A E A   E   F#m   D   A
Mmm,___   whoa, oh.

Verse 1
N.C.   E   A
Could I wake up next to you when it's hitting double figures,
E   A
Look into your eyes like I'm looking into double mirrors.
E   F#m   D
Could you make it any clearer, everything's such a blur,
A   E
It's not my turn, it's hers to get hurt.
     A   E
On a late night coming home from way too many train rides,
     A   E   F#m
Lace not as red as my face, I'm home at the same time.
                       D   A
Highbury estate's fine, smoking like a dragon, but don't chase lines.
         E   (F#m)
Hey.___

Pre-chorus 1
   F#m   D   A
     I haven't slept for the past week,
      E   F#m
And two hours ain't enough for me,
     D   E
I feel inspired at quarter to three A.M.
F#m   D   A
   I haven't changed since our last meet,
      E   F#m
I'm still getting all my meals for free,
                D   A   E
I think I'm being shunned by my feet again.

Chorus 1

    A   E   A
    'Cause it's not a homeless life for me,
                                  E   F♯m
It's just I'm home less than I'd like to be.
                          D   A
And it's not a homeless life for me,
                                  E   A
It's just I'm home less than I'd like to be.
                            E   A
And it's not a homeless life for me,
                                  E   F♯m
It's just I'm home less than I'd like to be.
                          D   A
And it's not a homeless life for me, yeah

Verse 2

N.C.   E   A
And now I'm sitting on a night bus flicking through my iPod,
E   A
Feeling kinda tired so I try to close my eyes up.
E   F♯m   D
Driver, turn the lights off, lights on, on stage, mics on,
A   E
Song plays, nice one, gotta keep my hype strong.
A   E   A
Truth be, never went to uni, people see right through me,
                            E   F♯m
But I'm not a fool, see, I'm never gonna do one.
                        D
Gonna live past twenty-two, done,
A   E   (F♯m)
Everything I need to except get a two-one.

Pre-chorus 2 as Pre-chorus 1

Chorus 2 as Chorus 1

     E   F#m
When I __ feel cold,
     D   A
  You keep me warm.
     E   F#m
  And I'm not looking for some loose change,
      E   D
Just wanna find a true mate who wants to be my duvet hey, hey.

Chorus 3

     A   E   A
  It's not a homeless life for me,
                        E   F#m
It's just I'm home less than I'd like to be.
                 D   A
And it's not a homeless life for me,
                        E   A
It's just I'm home less than I'd like to be.
                 E   A
And it's not a homeless life for me,
                        E   F#m
It's just I'm home less than I'd like to be.
                 D   A
And it's not a homeless life for me,
                        E   A
It's just I'm home less than I'd like to be.
                 E   A
And it's not a homeless life for me,
                        E   F#m
It's just I'm home less than I'd like to be.
                 D   A
And it's not a homeless life for me,
                        E   A
It's just I'm home less than I'd like to be.
                 E   A
And it's not a homeless life for me,
                        E   F#m
It's just I'm home less than I'd like to be.
                 D   A   E   A
And it's not a homeless life for me, yeah, mmm, oh.

HOW WOULD YOU FEEL (PAEAN)

Words & Music by Ed Sheeran

G   G/B   Cadd9   Bm7   Em   A7   D   Am

Capo 2

Intro | G   G/B | Cadd9 | G   G/B | Cadd9 |

Verse 1

G   G/B   Cadd9
You are the one girl
                         G G/B   Cadd9
And you know that it's true.
G   G/B   Cadd9
I'm feeling younger
                               G G/B   Cadd9
Every time that I'm alone with you.
Bm7
    We were sitting in a parked car,
Em
  Stealing kisses in the front yard,
A7   D
  We got questions we should not ask, but

Chorus 1

N.C.   G   G/B Cadd9
How would you feel,
                  G   G/B   Cadd9
If I told you I loved you?
                         G   G/B   Cadd9
It's just something that I want to do.
                  Am   D
I'll be taking my time,   spending my life____
                      G G/B Cadd9
Falling deeper in love with you.
                    G G/B Cadd9
So tell me that you love me too.

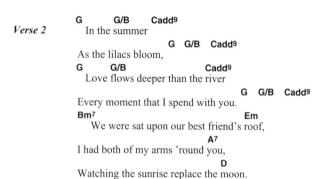

Verse 2

     G   **G/B**   **Cadd⁹**
    In the summer

                    G **G/B**   **Cadd⁹**
As the lilacs bloom,

G   **G/B**   **Cadd⁹**
  Love flows deeper than the river

                               G **G/B** **Cadd⁹**
Every moment that I spend with you.

Bm⁷   **Em**
    We were sat upon our best friend's roof,

                    A⁷
I had both of my arms 'round you,

                        D
Watching the sunrise replace the moon.

Chorus 2 as Chorus 1

Instrumental | **G**   **G/B** | **Cadd⁹** | **G**   **G/B** | **Cadd⁹** |

               | **G**   **G/B** | **Cadd⁹** | **G**   **G/B** | **Cadd⁹** |

Verse 3

    Bm⁷
    We were sitting in a parked car,

    Em
    Stealing kisses in the front yard.

    A⁷   **D**
    We got questions we should not ask.

N.C.   **G   G/B   Cadd9**

How would you feel,

                 G   G/B   Cadd9

If I told you I loved you?

                            G   G/B   Cadd9

It's just something that I want to do.

                 Am   **D**

I'll be taking my time,   spending my life___

                   G   G/B   Cadd9

Falling deeper in love with you.

                   G   G/B   Cadd9

So tell me that you love me too.

                   G   G/B   Cadd9

Tell me that you love me too.

                   G   G/B   Cadd9

Tell me that you love me too.

I SEE FIRE

Words & Music by Ed Sheeran

Am **Fmaj7** **G** fr3 **C** **Dsus2** **Dm**

To match original recording, tune guitar up one semitone

N.C.

Intro
Oh, misty eye of the mountain below,

Keep careful watch of my brothers' souls.

And should the sky be filled with fire and smoke,
                                   Am
Keep watching over Durin's sons.

Link 1 | Am Fmaj7 | G Am | Am Fmaj7 | G Am ‖

Verse 1
Am   **C**   **G**   **Fmaj7**
If this is to end in fire, then we should all burn to - gether,
         Am   **C** **G**   **Dsus2**
Watch the flames climb high into the night.
         Am   **C** **G**   **Fmaj7**
Calling out father,   oh, stand by and we will
          Dm   **C**   **Fmaj7**
Watch the flames burn auburn on the mountain side high.

Link 2 | Am Fmaj7 | G Am ‖

Verse 2
Am   **C**   **G**   **Fmaj7**
And if we should die to - night, then we should all die to - gether,
         Am   **C** **G**   **Dsus2**
Raise a glass of wine for the last time.
         Am   **C** **G**   **Fmaj7**
Calling out father,   oh, prepare as we will
          Dm   **C**   **Fmaj7**
Watch the flames burn auburn on the mountain side,
       Dm **C**   **Fmaj7**
Deso - lation comes upon the sky.

Chorus 1

(Fmaj7)   Am Fmaj7 G   Am
Now, I see fire   inside the mountain,

         Fmaj7 G   Am
I see fire   burning the trees.

           Fmaj7 G   Am
And I see fire_____ hollowing souls,

         Fmaj7 G   Dsus2
I see fire,_____ blood in the breeze.

And I hope that you remember me.

Link 3

| Am Fmaj7 | G Am | Am Fmaj7 | G Am | ‖

Verse 3

Am   C   G   Fmaj7
Oh, should my people fall, then surely I'll do the same,

         Am   C   G   Dsus2
Confined in mountain halls, we got too close to the flame.

     Am   C G   Fmaj7
Calling out father, oh, hold fast and we will

        Dm   C   Fmaj7
Watch the flames burn auburn on the mountain side,

      Dm C   Fmaj7
Deso - lation comes upon the sky.

Chorus 2

As Chorus 1

Bridge

Dsus2   Dm   Am   C   G
And if the night is burning, I will cover my eyes,

         Dm   Am   C   G
For if the dark re - turns, then my brothers will die.

         Dm   Am   C   G
And as the sky is falling down it crashed in - to this lonely town,

         Dm
And with that shadow upon the ground

C   Fmaj7   G
I hear my people screaming out.__

Chorus 3

(G)   Am   Fmaj7   G   Am
Now, I see fire   inside the mountain,

     Fmaj7   G   Am
I see fire   burning the trees.

     Fmaj7   G   Am
And I see fire_____ hollowing souls,

     Fmaj7   G   Am
I see fire,_____ blood in the breeze.

Outro

Am   Fmaj7   G   Am
I see fire, oh   you know I saw a city burning.

     Fmaj7   G   Am
And I see fire, feel the heat upon my skin, yeah.

     Fmaj7   G   Am
And I see fire, ooh._____

     Fmaj7   G   Am
And I see fire burn auburn on the mountain side.

I WILL TAKE YOU HOME

Words & Music by Ed Sheeran & John McDaid

D	A5	B5	G5
×○ × 5fr	× × 7fr	×× × 9fr	×× × 5fr

Intro | D | D | D | D |

Verse 1

D   A5   B5
  I stole a car last night,
A5   D   G5
    Don't know where we're gonna go,
D   A5   B5
  But go ahead and drive,___
G5   A5   D
  I will take you home.
        A5   B5
Honey, it's cold outside
A5   D   G5
    And your jumper's torn,
D   A5   B5
  But darling, hold on tight,
G5   A5   D
  I will keep you warm.

Chorus 1

(D)   G5   D   A5
  And we will cry till this fire is drowned,
           G5   D   A5
And we will write all our memories down.
           G5   D   A5
And we will drive till these tires wear out,
  B5 A5 G5   A5   D
But darling I, I will take you home.

Instrumental ‖: D | A5 | B5 | B5 |

            | G5 | A5 | D | D   :‖

Verse 2

```
        D                A5              B5
     If we could drive all night
     A5           D                  G5
        Until the sun is shone up,
     D            A5           B5
     I'll see it in your eyes,   yeah,
           G5             A5            D
     Mmm,___they will take me home.
                 A5              B5
     Honey, it's so damn bright,
     A5           D            G5
        Daylight's taken over again.
     D            A5      B5      A5
     Just follow the signs, ooh,___
     G5              A5            D
        They will lead us home.___
```

Chorus 2 as Chorus 1

Chorus 3

```
     (D)              G5               D            A5
     And we will drive till these tires wear out,
                   G5          D           A5
     And we will write all our memories down.
                   G5          D       A5
     And we will cry till this fire is drowned,
          B5  A5  G5       A5                 B5
     But, darling, I, I will keep you warm,
              A5  G5     A5                B5
     Oh, darling, I, I will keep you warm,
              A5  G5     A5             D
     And darling, I, I will take you home.
```

I'M A MESS

Words & Music by Ed Sheeran

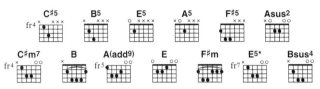

To match original recording, tune guitar down one semitone

Verse 1

     N.C.   C#5   B5
Oh, I'm a mess right now, inside out,

                      E5
Searching for a sweet surrender,

      A5   E5
But this is not the end.

    F#5 C#5   B5
I can't work it out how___

               E5
Going through the motions,

  A5   B5
Going through us.

Pre-chorus 1

   A5   E5
And, oh, I've known it for the longest time

            B5   A5
And all of my hopes, all of my own words

                    E5
Are all overwritten on the signs,

              B5
But you're on my road,

          Asus2
Walking me home, home, home, home, home.

Chorus 1

C#m7   B
See the flames inside my eyes,

           A(add9)   E   F#5
It burns so bright I wanna feel your love, no.___

C#m7   B
Easy baby, maybe I'm a liar,

           A(add9)   E
But for to - night I wanna fall in love

              F#m   A(add9)
And put your faith in my stomach.

Verse 2

N.C.   C#5   B5
I messed it up this time, late last night.

                 E5
Drinking to sup - press devotion

     A5   E5
With fingers inter - twined.

F#5 C#5   B5
I can't shake this feeling now,___

                 E
We're going through the motions,

Asus2   B5
Hoping you'd stop.

Pre-chorus 2

          Asus2
And oh, I've only caused you pain,

    E   B5   A5
I know but all of my words will always below

               E
Of all the love you spoke,

             B5
When you're on my road,

           Asus2
Walking me home, home, home, home, home.

Chorus 2   As Chorus 1

Bridge

        C#5 E5* B5   A5 E B5 C#5
And for how long I love____my lov - er,

        C#5 E5* B5   A5 E B5 C#5
For how long I love____my lov - er. And now, now,

        C#5 E5* B5   A5 E B5 C#5
For how long, long, I love____my lov - er, now, now,

        C#5 E5* B5   A5 E B5 C#5
For how long, long, I love____my lov - er, now, now.

(cont. in background)

        C#m7 E5* B5   Asus2 E Bsus4 C#m7
(For how long, long, I love_____ my lov - er, now, now.)

        C#m7   E5* Bsus4
And I feel loved.

        Asus2 E   Bsus4 C#m7   E5* Bsus4
I feel it all   over now, now and I feel loved.

        Asus2 E   Bsus4 C#m7   E5* Bsus4
I feel it all   over now, now and I feel loved.

        Asus2 E   Bsus4 C#m7   E5* Bsus4
I feel it all   over now, now and I feel loved.

        Asus2 E   Bsus4 C#m7   E5* Bsus4
I feel it all   over now, now and I feel loved.

        Asus2 E   Bsus4 C#m7
I feel it all   over now, now and I feel loved.

Outro

        C#5 E5* B5   A5 E B5 C#5
For how long I love____ my lov - er now, now,

        C#5 E5* B5   A5 B5 C#5
For how long I love____ my lover.

KISS ME

Words & Music by Ed Sheeran, Julie Frost & Justin Franks

Intro

‖: D | D A | Bm⁷ | Bm⁷ A :‖

| G | G A | D | D :‖

Verse 1

D   A   Bm⁷
Settle down with me,

A   G   A   D
Cover me up, cuddle me in.

A   Bm⁷
Lie down with me

A   G   A   D
And hold___ me in your arms.

Pre-chorus 1

G   A
   And your heart's against my chest,

D
Your lips pressed to my neck,

Bm⁷   G
I'm falling for your eyes, but they don't know me yet.

A   N.C.
And with a feeling I'll for - get, I'm in love now.

Chorus 1

D   A   Bm⁷
Kiss me like you wanna be loved,

A   G   A   D
You wanna be loved, you wanna be loved.

A   Bm⁷
This feels like falling in love,

A   G   A   D
Falling in love, we're falling in love.

Verse 2

      D   A   Bm7
Settle down with me

               A   G   A   D
And I'll be your safe - ty, you'll be my la - dy.

            A   Bm7
I was made   to keep your body warm,

   A   G   A   D
   But I'm cold as the wind blows   so hold me in your arms.

Pre-chorus 2   As Pre-chorus 1

Chorus 2   As Chorus 1

Instrumental ‖: D | D A | Bm7 | Bm7 A |

                | G | G A | D | D   :‖

Bridge

      A   B♭dim7
Yeah, I've been feeling every - thing

                       Bm7
From hate to love, from love to lust, from lust to truth,

   A   G
I   guess that's how I know you.

    Gm
So hold you close to help you give it up.

Chorus 3

   D   A   Bm7
   So kiss me like you wanna be loved,

      A   G   A   D
You wanna be loved, you wanna be loved.

              A   Bm7
This feels like falling in love,

   A   G   A   D
Falling in love, we're falling in love.

Chorus 4   As Chorus 1

Outro   ‖: D | D A | Bm7 | Bm7 A |

          | G | G A | D | D   :‖ *Fade out*

LAY IT ALL ON ME

Words & Music by Ed Sheeran, Edward Harris, Lasse Petersen, Kesi Dryden,
Piers Aggett, James Newman, James Wood, Max Mcelligott, Gavin Slater,
Adam Englefield, Jason Manson, Leon Rolle & Amir Izkadeh

G   A   Bm   D   Em7   F#m7

Capo 4

Intro ‖: G   A | Bm | G   A | Bm   D   :‖

Verse 1
G   A   Bm
All alone as you look through the door,
G   A   Bm
Nothing left to see.
G   A   Bm
If it hurts and you can't take no more,
G   A   Bm
Lay it all on me.

Pre-chorus 1
D   G   A   Bm
No, you don't have to keep it under lock and key,
        G   A   Bm
'Cause I will never let you down.
              G   A   Bm
And if you can't escape all your uncertainties,
G   A   Bm   D
Baby, I can show you how.

Chorus 1
G   A   Bm   D
Let my love in, let my love in,
G   A   Bm
Lay your heart on me.
G   A   Bm
And if you're hurting, if you're hurting,
            Em7   F#m7   Bm
You can   lay it all on me.
D   G   A   Bm
You can lay it all on me.
D   G   A   Bm   D
You can lay it all on me.
G   A   Bm
And if you're hurting, if you're hurting,
            Em7   F#m7   Bm
You can   lay it all on me.

Verse 2
```
    G            A                Bm
     If you're scared when you're out on your own,
    G       A       Bm
     Just remember me.
    G            A              Bm
     'Cause I won't let you go it alone,
    G       A    Bm
     Lay it all on me.
```

Pre-chorus 2 as Pre-chorus 1

Chorus 2 as Chorus 1

Bridge
```
    G                A      Bm              D
     So if you're hurting babe, just let your heart be free,
    G         A         D
     You got a friend in me.
    G         A      Bm   D
     I'll be your shoulder at anytime you need,
    G       A    D
     Baby, I believe.
    G                A      Bm              D
     So if you're hurting babe, just let your heart be free,
    Em7          F#m7    G
      You got a friend in me.
                 A       Bm    D
     I'll be your shoulder at anytime you need,
    Em7     F#m7  G
      Baby, I be - lieve.
             Em7        F#m7  G
    You can lay it all on    me.
```

Chorus 3

G   A   Bm
Let my love in, let my love in,
G   A   Bm   D
Lay your heart on me.
G   A   Bm
And if you're hurting, if you're hurting,
       Em7   F♯m7 Bm
You can   lay it all on me.
D   G   A   Bm
You can lay it all on me.
D   Em7   F♯m7 Bm
You can   lay it all on me.
G   A   Bm
If you're hurting, if you're hurting,
       Em7   F♯m7 Bm
You can   lay it all on me.

Chorus 4

G   A Bm   D
Lay it all,   lay it all on me,
Em7   F♯m7 Bm
    Lay it all on me.
G   A Bm   D
Lay it all,   lay it all on me,
Em7   F♯m7 Bm
    Lay it all on me.
G   A Bm   D
Lay it all,   lay it all on me,
Em7   F♯m7 Bm
    Lay it all on me.
N.C.
Lay it all, lay it all on me,

Lay it all on me.

LEGO HOUSE

Words & Music by Ed Sheeran, Christopher Leonard & Jake Gosling

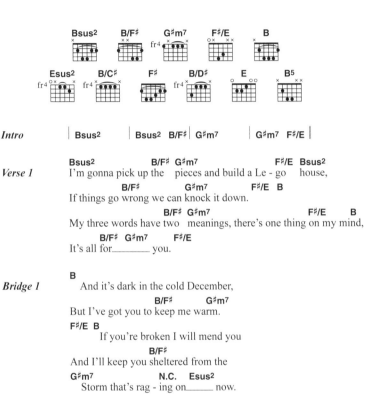

Intro | Bsus² | Bsus² B/F♯ | G♯m⁷ | G♯m⁷ F♯/E ‖

Verse 1

Bsus²   B/F♯ G♯m⁷   F♯/E Bsus²
I'm gonna pick up the pieces and build a Le - go house,
    B/F♯   G♯m⁷   F♯/E B
If things go wrong we can knock it down.
      B/F♯ G♯m⁷   F♯/E   B
My three words have two meanings, there's one thing on my mind,
   B/F♯ G♯m⁷   F♯/E
It's all for_____ you.

Bridge 1

 B
  And it's dark in the cold December,
      B/F♯   G♯m⁷
But I've got you to keep me warm.
F♯/E B
    If you're broken I will mend you
    B/F♯
And I'll keep you sheltered from the
G♯m⁷   N.C. Esus²
  Storm that's rag - ing on_____ now.

Chorus 1

B   B/C♯   G♯m7
  I'm out of touch, I'm out of love,

          B   F♯
I'll pick you up when you're getting down.

      B/D♯   E
And out of all these things I've done,

      F♯   B
I think I love you better now.

       B/C♯   G♯m7
I'm out of sight, I'm out of mind,

       B/C♯ F♯
I'll do it all for you in time.

       B/D♯   E
And out of all these things I've done,

      F♯   B
I think I love you better now.

   G♯m7 Esus2
Now.

Verse 2

Bsus2   B/F♯ G♯m7   Esus2 Bsus2
 I'm gonna paint you by numbers and colour you in,

      B/F♯   G♯m7   Esus2 Bsus2
If things go right we can frame it and put you on a wall.

        B/F♯ G♯m7   Esus2 Bsus2
And it's so hard to say it, but I've been here be - fore,

        B/F♯ G♯m7   Esus2
Now I'll surrender up my heart and swap it for yours.

Chorus 2

B   B/C♯   G♯m7
  I'm out of touch, I'm out of love,

          B   F♯
I'll pick you up when you're getting down.

      B/D♯   E
And out of all these things I've done,

      F♯   B
I think I love you better now.

       B/C♯   G♯m7
I'm out of sight, I'm out of mind,

       B   F♯
I'll do it all for you in time.

       B/D♯   E
And out of all these things I've done,

      F♯
I think I love you better now.

Middle

G♯m7   F♯   E
Don't hold me down,___

      F♯
I think the braces are breaking

    E   F♯
And it's more than I can take.___

Bridge 2

B
And it's dark in the cold December,

        B/F♯   G♯m7
But I've got you to keep me warm.

F♯/E B
If you're broken I will mend you

        B/F♯
And I'll keep you sheltered from the

G♯m7   F♯/E
Storm that's raging on now.

Chorus 3   As Chorus 2

Chorus 4

B5   B/C♯   G♯m7
I'm out of touch, I'm out of love,

             B5   B/F♯
I'll pick you up when you're getting down.

          G♯m7   Esus2
And out of all these things I've done,

         B/F♯   B5
I will love you better now.

LET IT OUT

Words & Music by Ed Sheeran

E   B5   C#m7   A5   Amaj7   B6/D#

Capo 4

⑥ = E   ③ = G#
⑤ = A   ② = B
④ = D   ① = E

Intro   ‖: E | B5 | C#m7 | A5   Amaj7 :‖

Verse 1
E   B5   C#m7   A5   Amaj7 E   B5   C#m7   A5   Amaj7
You give me life like lots of oxygen,
E   B5   C#m7 A5   Amaj7 E   B5   C#m7   A5   Amaj7
You treat me like I was in love again.
E   B5   C#m7 A5   Amaj7 E   B5   C#m7   A5   Amaj7
And I hold you tight, tight enough to know__
E   B5   C#m7   A5   Amaj7 E   B5   C#m7
That you are mine, I'd never let you go._____

Pre-chorus 1
A5   Amaj7 C#m7 B6/D# E A   C#m7 B6/D#   E
And it's   you_____   I miss.
A5   Amaj7 C#m7 B6/D# E A   C#m7 B6/D#   E
And it's   you_____   I miss.

Chorus 1
A5   E B5 C#m7
So let it out,_____
A5   Amaj7   E B5 C#m7
And let it   out_____ now.
A5   Amaj7   E B5 C#m7
And let it   out,_____
A5   Amaj7   E B5 C#m7 A5   Amaj7
And let it   out_____ now,   now.

Link   ‖: E | B5 | C#m7 | A5   Amaj7 :‖

Verse 2
E   B5   C#m7   A5   Amaj7 E   B5 C#m7 A5 Amaj7
And you speak to me behind your dark green stare,
E   B5   C#m7 A5   Amaj7 E   B5 C#m7 A5 Amaj7
And you've   let me be   as if I wasn't there.____

	E B5 C#m7
Bridge 1	It seemed perfect, the concept, free from any regret,

Bridge 1

      E   **B5**   **C#m7**

It seemed perfect, the concept, free from any regret,

            A5   **Amaj7**   **E**

Another couple based on teen   sex,   you idiot.

B5   **C#m7**

True, I was just like you, we couldn't be torn apart,

          A5   **Amaj7**

You see we were just like glue.

Bridge 1 — **E** / **B5** / **C#m7** / **A5** / **Amaj7** / **E** / **B5** / **C#m7** / **A5** / **Amaj7**

Pre-chorus 2 as Pre-chorus 1

Chorus 2 as Chorus 1

Bridge 2 as Bridge 1

| *Bridge 3* | ‖: **E**   **B5**   :‖ *Repeat 4 times* |

Bridge 3   ‖: **E**   **B5**   :‖ *Repeat 4 times*

    Like glue, we're like glue, we're like glue.

C#m7   **A5**

    Like glue, we're like glue, we're like glue.

Chorus 3 as Chorus 1

            E   **B5**   **C#m7**

Bridge 4   It seemed perfect, the concept, free from any regret,

              A5   **Amaj7**   **E**

Another couple based on teen   sex, you idiot.

B5   **C#m7**

True, I was just like you, we couldn't be torn apart,

          A5   **N.C.**

You see we were just like glue.

LITTLE BIRD

Words & Music by Ed Sheeran

Bm   G   D   A/C♯   A   B♭dim7

Capo sixth fret

Intro

| Bm | G | D | D A/C♯ ‖

Verse 1

Bm   G
If we take this bird in   with its broken leg,
D   A/C♯
We could nurse it, she said.
Bm   G
Come inside for a little lie down with me,
D   A/C♯
If you fall asleep it wouldn't be the worst thing.
            G   D
But when I wake up your make-up is on my shoulder,
A/C♯   G
And tell me, if I lie down would you stay now
          A
And let me hold you? Oh.

Chorus 1

B♭dim7   Bm
But if I kiss you will your mouth read this truth?   G
                D
Darling, how I miss you, strawberries taste how lips do.
A/C♯   Bm   G
And it's not com - plete yet, mustn't get our feet wet,
            D
'Cause that leads to regret, diving in too soon.
A/C♯   G   A   Bm
And I'll owe it all to you, oh,   my little bird,
G   D   A/C♯
My little bird.

Bm   G
If we take a walk out   in the morning dew,

D   A/C♯
We could lay down so I'm next to you.

Bm   G
And come inside for a little home-made tea,

D   A/C♯
And if you fall asleep, then at least you're next to me.

          G   D
And if I wake up you see, it's late, love, go back to sleep

A/C♯   G
I'm covered by nature and I'm safe now

                    A
Underneath this oak tree with you beside me.

B♭dim7   Bm   G
Chorus 2   But if I kiss you will your mouth read this truth?

                        D
Darling, how I miss you, strawberries taste how lips do.

A/C♯   Bm   G
And it's not com - plete yet, mustn't get our feet wet,

                        D
'Cause that leads to regret, diving in too soon.

A/C♯   G   A   G
And I'll owe it all to you, oh,   my little bird,

A   Bm   D
My little bird,

          G
My little bird,

A   Bm   D
My little bird.

          D   G   A
Bridge   And of all these things I'm sure of,

          G   A
I'm not quite certain of your love.

              G   A
And you made me scream, but then I made you cry

              G   A
When I left that little bird with its broken leg to die.

107

A Bm   G
But if I kiss you will your mouth read this truth?

       D
Darling, how I miss you, strawberries taste how lips do.

A/C♯   Bm   G
 And it's not com - plete yet, mustn't get our feet wet,

       D
'Cause that leads to regret, diving in too soon.

A/C♯ G   A   Bm G
 But I'll owe it all to you, oh, my little bird

    D   A/C♯
My little bird, whoa, oh, oh.

     Bm G
My little bird,

     D
My little bird,

A/C♯   G
You're my little bird.

MAKE IT RAIN

Words & Music by Foy Vance

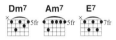

Dm7　　**Am7**　　**E7**

Tune guitar down one semitone

Intro　　‖: Dm7　　| Am7　　| E7　　| Am7　　:‖ *Repeat 3 times*

Verse 1

Dm7　　　　　　　　　　　Am7
　When the sins of my father
E7　　　　　　　　　Am7
　Weigh down in my soul,
Dm7　　　　　　　Am7
　And the pain of my mother
E7　　　　　　Am7
　Will not let me go.
Dm7　　　　　　　　　　　　Am7
　Well, I know there can come fire from the sky
　　E7　　　　　　　　　Am7
To refine the purest of kings,
Dm7　　　　　　　　　　Am7
　And even though I know this fire brings me pain,
　　E7　　　　　　Am7
Even so and just the same.

Chorus 1

(Am7)　　Dm7　　　　Am7
Make it rain, make it rain down, Lord,
　　　　　E7　　　　　Am7
Make it rain, oh, make it rain.
　　　　Dm7　　　　Am7
Make it rain, make it rain down, Lord,
　　　　E7　　　　Am7
Make it rain, make it rain.

Verse 2

Dm⁷   Am⁷
Oh, seed needs the water
E⁷   Am⁷
Before it grows out of the ground,
Dm⁷   Am⁷
But it just keeps on getting hard
E⁷   Am⁷
And the hunger more profound.
Dm⁷   Am⁷
Well, I know there can come tears from the eyes,
         E⁷   Am⁷
But they may as well all be in vain.
Dm⁷   Am⁷
Even though I know these tears come with pain,
      E⁷   Am⁷
Even so and just the same.

Chorus 2 as Chorus 1

Instrumental ‖: Dm⁷ | Am⁷ | E⁷ | Am⁷   :‖

Dm⁷   Am⁷
Verse 3 And the seas are full of water
E⁷   Am⁷
That stops by the shore.
Dm⁷   Am⁷
Just like the riches of grandeur
E⁷   Am⁷
That never reach the poor.
Dm⁷   Am⁷
And let the clouds fill with thunderous applause,
      E⁷   Am⁷
And let lightning be the veins.
Dm⁷   Am⁷
And fill the sky with all that they can drop,
       E⁷   Am⁷
When it's time to make a change.

(Am7)   Dm7   Am7
Make it rain, make it rain down, Lord,
        E7   Am7
Make it rain, oh, make it rain.
        Dm7   Am7
Make it rain, make it rain down, Lord,
        E7   Am7
Make it rain, oh, make it rain.
        Dm7   Am7
Make it rain, make it rain,
        E7   Am7
Make it rain, oh, make it rain.
        Dm7   Am7
Make it rain, make it rain down, Lord,
        E7   Am7
Make it rain, oh, make it rain.
        Dm7   Am7
Make it rain, make it rain,
        E7   Am7
Make it rain, make it rain.
        Dm7   Am7
Make it rain, make it rain,
        E7   Am7
Make it rain, oh, make it rain.

THE MAN

Words & Music by Ed Sheeran

[Chord diagrams: A, Bm, F#m, G]

Intro | A | Bm | F#m | G   A | Bm | F#m | G   A ‖

Verse 1

(A)   **Bm**
Now I don't wanna hate you, just wish you'd never gone for the man
F#m G   **A   Bm**
    And waited two weeks at least before you let him take you.
                                              F#m
I stayed true, I kind of knew you liked the dude from private school,
      G   **A   Bm**
He's waiting for the time to move, I knew he had his eyes on you.
                                        F#m
He's not the right guy for you, don't hate me cause I write the truth,
      G   **A Bm**
No, I would never lie to you, but it was never fine to lose you.
                              F#m
And what a way to find out, it never came from my mouth,
                                              A   Bm
You never changed your mind, but you were just a - fraid to mind out
                              F#m
But fuck it, I won't be changing the subject I love it,
G
 I'll make your little secret public, it's nothing.
A   Bm   **F#m**
   I'm just disgusted with the skeletons you sleep with in your closet
        G
To get back at me.

Trapped and I'm lacking sleep,
        A   Bm   **F#m**
The fact is you're mad at me because I backtrack so casually.

112

     G
You're practically my family,
              A   **Bm**
If we married then I'll guess you'd have to be.
                     F♯m
But tragically our love just lost the will to live,
         G
But would I kill to give it one more shot, I think not.

Chorus 1
A Bm   **F♯m**   **G**
I don't love you baby, I don't need you baby,
A Bm   **F♯m**   **G**
I don't want you, no, anymore.____
A Bm   **F♯m**   **G**
I don't love you baby, I don't need you baby,
A Bm   **F♯m**   **G**
I don't wanna love you, no, anymore.____

Verse 2
(G)   **A**   **Bm**
Recently I tend to zone out up in my headphones to "Holocene",
    F♯m   **G**
You promised your body but I'm away so much
              A   **Bm**
I stay more celi - bate than in a monastery.
                 F♯m
I'm not cut out for life on the road
       G
'Cause I didn't know I'd miss you this much
         A   **Bm**
And at the time we'd just go, so sue me,
           F♯m
I guess I'm not the man that you need,
    G   **A**   **Bm**
Ever since you went to uni, I've been sofa surfing with a rucksack,
                     F♯m
Full of less cash and I guess that could get bad.
        G
But when I broke the industry, that's when I broke your heart,
A Bm   **F♯m**
  I was supposed to chart and celebrate, but good things are over fast.
G
I know it's hard to deal with and see this,
        A   **Bm**
I tend to turn you off and switch on my professional features.

       F♯m   G
Then I turn the music off

                                    A   Bm
And all I'm left with is to pick up my per - sonal pieces.

                      F♯m
Jesus, I never really want to be - lieve this,

        G
Got ad - vice from my dad

                  A   Bm
And he told me that family is all I'll ever have and need,

                    F♯m   G
I guess I'm unaware of it: suc - cess is nothing

If you have no one there left to share it with.

Chorus 2   As Chorus 1

              (G)   A   Bm
Verse 3   And since you left, I've given up my days off,

                        F♯m
It's what I need to stay strong,

         G   A   Bm
I know you have a day job but mine is twenty four se - ven.

I feel like writing a book, I guess I lied in the hook,

F♯m
  'Cause I still love you and I need you by my side if I could.

A Bm
  The irony is if my career and music didn't exist,

F♯m   G
  In six years, yeah, you'd probably be my wife with a kid.

A Bm
  I'm frightened to think if I depend on cider and drink,

F♯m   G
  And lighting a spliff, I fall into a spiral and it's

A Bm
  Just hiding my misguiding thoughts that I'm trying to kill,

F♯m   G
  And I'd be writing my will before I'm twenty seven,

A Bm   F♯m
I'll die from a thrill, go down in history as just a wasted talent

      G   A   Bm
Can I face the challenge, or did I make a mistake e - rasing?

                                                              F♯m
It's only therapy, my thoughts just get a - head of me,

        G   A   Bm
E - ventually I'll be fine I know that it was never meant to be.

                                                F♯m   G
Either way I guess I'm not prepared, but I'll say this,

                                                A   Bm
These things happen for a reason and you can't change.

                                        F♯m
Take my apology, I'm sorry for the honesty,

        G
But I had to get this off my chest.

Chorus 3   As Chorus 1

Outro   A ‖: Bm   F♯m │ G   A │ Bm   F♯m │ G   A :‖

                                                  Repeat to fade

NEW MAN

Words & Music by Ed Sheeran,
Benjamin Levin, Ammar Malik & Jessica Ware

Em   G   D   C   Bm

Intro

| Em | G | D | Em |

| C | Bm | D | Em |

Verse 1

N.C.   G
I heard he spent five hundred pounds on jeans,
D   Em
  Goes to the gym at least six times a week.
C   Bm
  Wears boat shoes with no socks on his feet,
        D   Em
And I hear he's on a new diet and watches what he eats.
                                     G
He's got his eyebrows plucked and his arsehole bleached,
D   Em
Owns every single Ministry CD.
C   Bm
Tribal tattoos and he don't know what it means,
        D   Em
But I heard he makes you happy so that's fine by me.
N.C.   G
But still, I'm just keeping it real,
              D   Em
Still looking at your Instagram and I'll be creeping a little.
        C   Bm
I'll be trying not to double tap   from way back,
        D   Em
'Cause I know that's where the trouble's at.
                         N.C. G
Let me remind you of the days when you used to hold my hand,
              D   Em
And when we sipped champagne out of cider cans.
              C   Bm
I guess if you were Lois Lane, I wasn't superman,
        D   Em
Just a young boy trying to be loved, so let me give it to you.

```
Em                        G
    I don't wanna know about your new man,
D                 Em
  'Cause if it was meant to be,
C                        Bm
  You wouldn't be calling me up trying to,
            D                   Em
  'Cause I'm positive that he don't wanna know about me.
                     G
I don't wanna know about your new man,
D               Em
  We'll get there eventually.
C                      Bm
  I know you're missing all this kind of love,
         D                   Em
But I'm positive that he don't wanna know about me.
```

Verse 2

N.C.   G

Your new man rents a house in the 'burb,

                 D   Em

And wears a man bag on his shoulder but I call it a purse.

           C   Bm

Every year he goes to Malaga with all the fellas,

           D   Em

Drinks beer but has a six pack, I'm kind of jealous.

                              G

He wears sunglasses indoors in winter at night-time,

         D   Em

And every time a rap song comes on he makes a gun sign.

      C   Bm

Says tune, boy dem light up the room,

      D   Em

But enough about him, girl let's talk about you.

                                   G

You were the type of girl that sat beside the water reading,

         D   Em

Eating a packet of crisps, but you will never find you cheating.

           C   Bm   D

Now you're eating kale, hitting the gym, keeping up with Kylie and Ki*

           Em

In the back of the club kissing a boy that ain't him.

         G

Ok, you need to be alone,

         D   Em

And if you wanna talk about it you can call my phone.

      C   Bm

I just thought that I would tell you 'cause you oughta know,

          N.C.

You're still a young girl trying to be loved, so let me give it to you.

Chorus 2 as Chorus 1

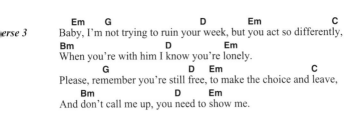

                    Em   G   D   Em   C
erse 3   Baby, I'm not trying to ruin your week, but you act so differently,
            Bm   D   Em
            When you're with him I know you're lonely.
                         G   D   Em   C
            Please, remember you're still free, to make the choice and leave,
                 Bm   D   Em
            And don't call me up, you need to show me.

Chorus 3 as Chorus 1

                    Em   G
Outro   I'm positive that he don't wanna know about me.
            D   Em
                I'm positive that he don't wanna know about me.
            C Bm   D   Em
                I don't wanna know about your new man.

NANCY MULLIGAN

Words & Music by Ed Sheeran, Benjamin Levin,
John McDaid, Foy Vance, Amy Wadge & Murray Cummings

Em	C	D	G

Verse 1

Em   C
I was twenty four years old
       D   Em
When I met the woman I would call my own.
                         C   G
Twenty two grand kids now growing old
                C   D   Em
In the house that your brother bought you.
                        C
On the summer day when I proposed,
   D   Em
I made that wedding ring from dentist gold.
                         C   G
And I asked her father but her daddy said, no,
C   D   Em
You can't marry my daughter.

Chorus 1

G   C   G
She and I went on the run,
D   C   G
Don't care about religion.
                      C   G
I'm gonna marry the woman I love
C   D   Em
Down by the Wexford border.
G   C   G
She was Nancy Mulligan
      D   C   G
And I was William Sheeran.
                        C   G
She took my name and then we were one,
C   D   Em
Down by the Wexford border.

Link

Em		Em	C		D		Em	

Em		C	G		C	D		Em	

120

C

Verse 2 (Em)
Well, I met her at Guy's in the second world war
 D   Em
And she was working on a soldier's ward.
         C   G
Never had I seen such beauty before,
 C   D   Em
The moment that I saw her.
               C
Nancy was my yellow rose
 D   Em
And we got married wearing borrowed clothes.
            C   G
We got eight children now growing old,
C   D   Em
Five sons and three daughters.

Chorus 2 as Chorus 1

Instrumental ‖: G | G | D | D |

 | G | G | D | G   :‖

Verse 3 (G)   Em   C
From her snow white streak in her jet black hair,
      D   Em
Over sixty years I've been loving her.
                      C   G
Now we're sat by the fire, in our old armchairs,
         C   D Em
You know Nancy I adore you.
                        C
From a farm boy born near Belfast town,
D   Em
And I never worried about the king and crown.
                    C   G
Cause I found my heart upon the southern ground,
        C   D Em
There's no difference, I assure you.

Chorus 3 as Chorus 1

Outro　　‖: G　　　| C　　G　| D　　　　| D　　　　|

　　　　　| G　　　| C　　G　| D　　　　| G　　　　:‖

NEW YORK

Words & Music by Ed Sheeran & Emile Haynie

| Am7 | G | C | G/B | F |

Capo 6

Intro

| Am7 | G | C | C |

Ooh.—

| Am7 | G | C | C G/B |

Ooh.——————

Verse 1

C   G   C   G/B   Am7
    Five drinks in on Friday night, we only came to dry your eyes

     F   C   G
And get you out of your room.

C   G   C   G/B
    And now this bar has closed its doors, I found my hand is holding yours.

Am7   F   C
    Do you wanna go home so soon?

Pre-chorus 1

     G   F   C
Or maybe we should take a ride through the night

          G   Am7   F
And sing along to every song that's on the radio

C   G
    In the back of a taxi cab in Brooklyn all night long.

            C   G   Am7   F
The sun could rise burning all the street lamps out at three A.M.

       C   G
So, DJ, play it again.

Chorus 1

  (G)   C   F   Am7   G   C
Until the night turns into morning, you'll be in my arms.

          F   Am7   G   C
And we'll just keep driving along the boulevard.

        F   Am7   G   F
And if I kissed you, darling, please don't be alarmed.

         G   C
It's just the start of everything, if you want

   G   C   G   C
A new love in New York.

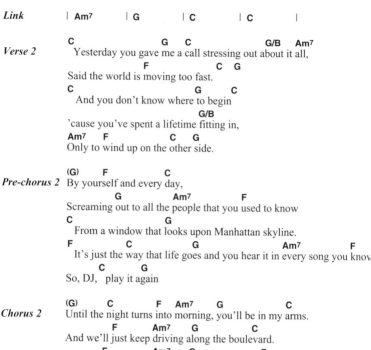

Link | Am7 | G | C | C |

Verse 2

   C   G   C   G/B   Am7
Yesterday you gave me a call stressing out about it all,

                      F   C   G
Said the world is moving too fast.

C   G   C
 And you don't know where to begin

                         G/B
'cause you've spent a lifetime fitting in,

Am7   F   C   G
Only to wind up on the other side.

Pre-chorus 2

 (G)   F   C
By yourself and every day,

           G   Am7   F
Screaming out to all the people that you used to know

C   G
 From a window that looks upon Manhattan skyline.

F   C   G   Am7   F
 It's just the way that life goes and you hear it in every song you know

       C   G
So, DJ, play it again

Chorus 2

 (G)   C   F   Am7   G   C
Until the night turns into morning, you'll be in my arms.

       F   Am7   G
And we'll just keep driving along the boulevard.

       F   Am7   G   F
And if I kissed you, darling, please don't be alarmed.

          G   C
It's just the start of everything, if you want

   G   C   G   C
A new life in New York.

Bridge

(C)   F   C   G   Am7
And every song that plays is just like the day you had,
    F   C   G   Am7
And it's okay to cry. But I'm saying maybe that's
  F   C   G   Am7   G
A waste of water, you know I'm here for you,
F   G
 In the back of the taxi cab tonight in New York.

Chorus 3

C   F   Am7   G   C
It's just reached the morning and you're still in my arms,
     F   Am7 G   C
And we've stopped driving down the boulevard.
        F   Am7   G   F
And I just kissed you, darling, I hope you weren't alarmed.
        G   C
It's just the start of everything that you want;
  G   C   G   C
A new love in New York.

NINA

Words & Music by Ed Sheeran, John McDaid,
Jermaine Scott, Jay Hippolyte & Isra Lohata

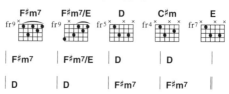

Intro

| F♯m7 | F♯m7/E | D | D | |
| D | D | F♯m7 | F♯m7 ||

Verse 1

N.C.   F♯m7   C♯m
I met you when I was a teen, but then you were one as well

        D
And I could play a guitar just like ringing a bell.

        E
Sometimes I wonder in any other summer could you have been

       F♯m7
My part time lover to me, listening to Stevie Wonder

        C♯m
Under the covers where we used to lay

D
And "Re: Stacks" is what the speakers played.

        E
I'd be on tour almost every day,

       F♯m7
When I was home up in my flat is where we used to stay.

Verse 2

F♯m7   C♯m
Just watching the DVD, smoking illegal weed,

D
    Getting high as two kites when we needed to breathe.

        E
We'd use each other's air just for the people to see,

F♯m7
    And stay up all night like when we needed to sleep.

We'd go anywhere, our minds would take us,

C♯m   D
    And I'd say you were beautiful without your make-up.

        E
And you don't even need to worry about your weight 'cause

cont.

F♯m7
We can all be loved the way that God made us.

And time's the only reason that we could break up,
C♯m D
 'Cause you would always tell me I'm away too much.
           E   F♯m7
Distance is relative to the time that it takes to get on a plane

Or make a mistake, so say it again.

Chorus 1
F♯m7   D
Oh Nina, you should go, Nina,

'Cause I ain't ever coming home, Nina
E   F♯m7
Oh, won't you leave me now.

And I've been living on the road, Nina,
         D
But then again you should know, Nina,

'Cause that's you and me both, Nina,
E   F♯m7
Oh, won't you leave me now, now.

Verse 3
F♯m7
And every weekend in the winter you'd be wearing my hoodie
  C♯m D
With draw-strings pulled tight to keep your face from the cold.
             E
Taking day trips to the local where we'd eat on our own,
    F♯m7
'Cause every day when I was away we'd only speak on the phone.

Watching "Blue Planet" creating new habits,
C♯m D
Acting as if we were two rabbits,

And then you'd vanish back to the burrow with all the Celtics.
E
I disappear, you call me selfish, I understand, but I can't help it.

I put my job over everything, except my family and friends,
  C♯m D
But you'll be in between forever

So I guess we'll have to take a step back,

| | E   F#m7 |
| *cont.* | Overlook the situ - ation, 'cause mixing business and feelings |

Will only lead to complications.

And I'm not saying we should be taking a break,

       C#m   D
Just re - e - valuate, quit before we make a mistake and it's too late.

                                   E   F#m7
So we can either deal with the pain or wait to get on a plane,

But in a day we'd have to say it again.

Chorus 2   As Chorus 1

             N.C.(F#m7)
Bridge   Love will come and love will go, but you can make it on your own.

Sing that song, go, oh won't you leave me now.

People grow and fall apart, but you can mend your broken heart,

Take it back, go, oh won't you leave me now.

(w/bridge lyrics in background)

             F#m7   D
Chorus 3   Oh Nina, you should go, Nina,

'Cause I ain't ever coming home, Nina
E   F#m7
Oh, won't you leave me now.

And I've been living on the road, Nina,

                      D
But then again you should know, Nina,

'Cause that's you and me both, Nina,
E   F#m7
Oh, won't you leave me now, now.

Chorus 4   As Chorus 3

Outro | F#m7 | F#m7/E | D | D |

               | D | D | F#m7 | F#m7   ‖

ONE

Words & Music by Ed Sheeran

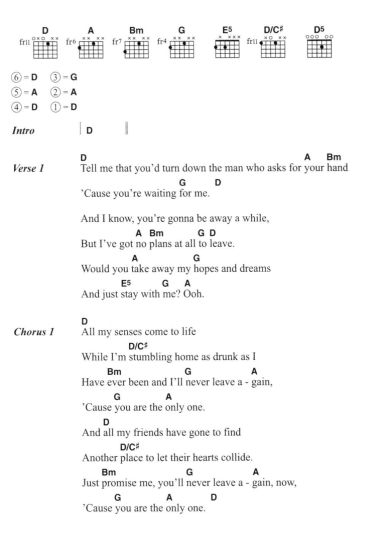

D   A   Bm   G   E5   D/C♯   D5

⑥ = **D** ③ = **G**
⑤ = **A** ② = **A**
④ = **D** ① = **D**

Intro | **D**   ‖

Verse 1
        D   **A**   **Bm**
Tell me that you'd turn down the man who asks for your hand
                         G   **D**
'Cause you're waiting for me.

And I know, you're gonna be away a while,
        A **Bm**   **G D**
But I've got no plans at all to leave.
           A   **G**
Would you take away my hopes and dreams
         E5   **G**   **A**
And just stay with me? Ooh.

Chorus 1
        D
All my senses come to life
           D/C♯
While I'm stumbling home as drunk as I
      Bm   **G**   **A**
Have ever been and I'll never leave a - gain,
        G   **A**
'Cause you are the only one.
        D
And all my friends have gone to find
         D/C♯
Another place to let their hearts collide.
      Bm   **G**   **A**
Just promise me, you'll never leave a - gain, now,
        G   **A**   **D**
'Cause you are the only one.

Verse 2

D   A
Take my hand and my heart and soul, I will
Bm   G   D
   Only have these eyes for you.

And you know, everything changes but
                    A   Bm   G   D
We'll be strang - ers if we see this through.
              A   G
We could stay within these walls and bleed
          E5   G   A
Or just stay with me, oh Lord, now

Chorus 2

D
All my senses come to life
              D/C♯
While I'm stumbling home as drunk as I
        Bm   G   A
Have ever been and I'll never leave a - gain, now,
        G   A
'Cause you are the only one.
              D
And all my friends have gone to find
              D/C♯
Another place to let their hearts collide.
        Bm   A
Just promise me, you'll always be a friend, now,
        G   A
'Cause you are the only one.

Bridge

G   D5   A
   Stumbling half drunk, getting myself lost,
              G   Bm   G
I am so gone, so tell me the way home.
              D5   G   A
I listen to sad songs, singing a - bout love
              (Bm)
And where it goes wrong.

| Bm G | D5 | Bm G | D5 | |
(wrong)_____

| Bm G | D5 | Bm A | G | G   ‖
___ ooh._____

Chorus 3

        D
All my senses come to life

               D/C♯
While I'm stumbling home as drunk as I

     Bm   **G**   **A**
Have ever been and I'll never leave a - gain,

        G   **A**
'Cause you are the only one.

       D
And all my friends have gone to find

         D/C♯
Another place to let their hearts collide.

     Bm   **A**
Just promise me, you'll always be a friend,

      G   **A**   **D5**
'Cause you are the only one.

ONE NIGHT

Words & Music by Ed Sheeran & Jake Gosling

Em   G   D   C   Am

Capo 2

Verse 1

Em   **G**
Lying in a bedroom, lighting up a Benson,

      D
Face hair is growing, so I cut it with a vengeance.

Em   **G**
Hey, did I mention, as she makes an entrance,

      D
Said I had a tendency to finish off a sentence.

Em   **G**
 Oh well, she's a local girl,

D
No make-up 'cause she knows me well.

Em   **G**
Hair tied up in elastic band,

     D
With a kiss on the cheek for her one-night man.

Pre-chorus 1

Em   **C**
 Is it fast food? I'll regret it after,

G
 And I needed money, but I'm too shy to ask her.

Em   **C**
 So she buys me chips and cheese

   G
And I tell her that I love her and she's all I need.

(G)   Em   G
I take it with a cold glass of the fruit and the barley,
D
She's still a sucker for the apple and Bacardi.
Em   G
Heading to the party sitting in the car seat
D   Em
B.E.P. on radio, it makes me feel naughty and lastly.
        G
She knows me well,
      D
A bit of a catch to have a local girl.
Em   G
Hair tied up in elastic band
          D
With a kiss on the cheek for her one-night man.

Am   D
I don't wanna go alone.
                          Am
I don't wanna go alone.
                          C   D
No, I don't wanna go alone.

(D)   Em   G
Tell her that I love her, tell her that I need her,
                       D
Tell her that she's more than a one-night stand.
                   Em   G
Tell her that she turns my cheeks the colour of my hair,
D
All I wanna do is be near.
               Em   G
Tell her that I want her, tell her that I need her,
                       D
Tell her that she's more than a one-night stand.
               Em   G
Tell her that I love her more than anyone else,
          D   N.C.
If you don't, I'll tell her myself.

Link 1   ‖: **Em** | **G** | **D** | **D**   :‖

Verse 3
N.C.   **Em**   **G**
And we've got that love in us, so if the drink kill us,
                D
We're gonna dance all night till the floor fillers.
        Em   **G**
If we talk outside, say I hate wasps too,
D
I don't really dance, so I'll just watch you.
            Em   **G**
Are you taking me back tonight, tell me if that's alright?
D
I don't wanna be here, I'm not the sofa type.
Em   **G**   **D**
Tell me if you have a toothbrush, you don't mind sharing,
                                    Am
She said I wanna take off what you're wearing.

Bridge 2
(Am)   **D**
And I don't wanna go alone.
                    Am
I don't wanna go alone.
                    C   **D**
I don't wanna go alone, oh.

Chorus 2 as Chorus 1

Link 2 as Link 1

Pre-chorus 2
Em   **C**
    She's like the fast food, I'll regret it after
G
    And I needed money, but I'm too shy to ask her
Em   **C**
    But she buys me chips and cheese,
        G
So I tell her that she's all I need.

134

       (G)   Em   G
Tell her that I, tell her that I
                        D
Tell her that she's more than a one-night stand.
                  Em   G
Tell her that she turns my cheeks the colour of my hair,
D
All I wanna do is be near.
                  Em   G
Tell her that I, tell her that I,
                        D
Tell her that she's more than a one-night stand.
                  Em   G
Tell her that I love her more than anyone else,
            D
If you don't, I'll tell her myself.

Chorus 4 as Chorus 1

THE PARTING GLASS

Words & Music by Ed Sheeran, Jake Gosling & Peter Gosling

F♯m   D   A/C♯   E   A   Bm   Esus⁴   E/G♯

Verse 1

    F♯m   D   A/C♯ E
Of all the money   that e'er I had,

     F♯m   D   A/C♯   E
I've spent it in___ good company.

     F♯m   D   A/C♯   E
And all the harm___ that e'er I've done,

      F♯m D A   D   E   F♯m
A - las   it was to none but me.

      A   D   A/C♯   D
And all I've done for want of wit,

    Bm   A/C♯ D   Esus⁴   E
To memo - ry   now I can't re - call.

    F♯m D   A   E/G♯
So fill to me the parting glass,

       F♯m   D   A   A/C♯ D   E   F♯m
Good night and joy be   with you all.

Verse 2

      F♯m   D   A/C♯ E
Of all the comrades that e'er I had,

        F♯m D   A/C♯   E
They are sorry for my going a - way.

      F♯m   D   A/C♯ E
And all the sweethearts that e'er I had,

         F♯m   A/C♯   D   E   F♯m
They would wish me one more day to stay.

     A   D   A/C♯   D
But since it falls un - to my lot,

    Bm   A/C♯   D   E
That I should rise and you should not.

    F♯m   D   A   E
I'll gently rise and I'll softly call,

       F♯m D   A   A/C♯ D   E   F♯m
Good night and joy be   with you all.

Verse 3

    F♯m   D   A/C♯   E
A man may drink and not be drunk,

    F♯m   D   A   E
A man may fight and not be slain.

    F♯m   D   A   E
A man may court a pretty girl,

         F♯m D A   A/C♯   D   E F♯m
And per - haps be wel - comed back a - gain.

   A   D   A/C♯   D
But since it has so ought to be,

    Bm   A/C♯   D   Esus2 E
By a time to rise and a time to fall.

    F♯m D   A   E
Come fill to me the parting glass,

    F♯m D A A/C♯ D   E   F♯m
Good night and joy be   with you all.

    F♯m D A A/C♯ D   E   F♯m
Good night and joy be   with you all.

PHOTOGRAPH

Words & Music by Ed Sheeran, Martin Harrington,
John McDaid & Tom Leonard

E   C#m   B   A

Intro

| E | E | C#m | C#m |

| B | B | A | A |

Verse 1

N.C.　　　E　　　　　　　C#m
Loving can hurt, loving can hurt sometimes,
　　　　　B　　　　　　　A
But it's the only thing that I know.
　　　　　　　　　E　　　　　　　　　C#m
And when it gets hard, you know it can get hard sometimes,
　　　　B　　　　　　　　　　A
It is the only thing that makes us feel alive.___

Pre-chorus 1

C#m　　　　　　　　　　A
　We keep this love in a photo - graph,
E　　　　　　　　　　B
　We made these memories for ourselves.
　　　C#m　　　　　A
Where our eyes are never closing, hearts are never broken
　E　　　　　　　　B
And times are forever frozen still.

Chorus 1

N.C.　　E　　　　　　　　　　　　　B
So you can keep me inside the pocket of your ripped jeans,
　　　　　　　C#m
Holding me closer till our eyes meet,
　　　　　　A　　　　　　　E
You won't ever be a - lone, wait for me to come home.

Verse 2

N.C.　　E　　　　　C#m
Loving can heal, loving can mend your soul
　　　　B　　　　　　　　　　A
And it's the only thing that I know, know.

138

                    E   C#m
I swear it will get easier, remember that with every piece of you,

                    B   A
And it's the only thing we take with us when we die.

Pre-chorus 2   As Pre-chorus 1

               N.C.   E   B
Chorus 2   So you can keep me inside the pocket of your ripped jeans,

                                    C#m
Holding me closer till our eyes meet,

                            A
You won't ever be a - lone.

                    E   B
And if you hurt me, that's okay baby, only words bleed.

                                C#m
Inside these pages you just hold me

                            A   C#m
And I won't ever let you go, wait for me to come home,

                    A
Wait for me to come home,

                    E
Wait for me to come home,

                    B
Wait for me to come home, ooh.

               (B)   E   B
Chorus 3   You can fit me inside the necklace you got when you were sixteen,

                                    C#m
Next to your heartbeat where I should be,

                            A
Keep it deep within your soul.

                    E   B
And if you hurt me, well, that's okay baby, only words bleed,

                                C#m
Inside these pages you just hold me

                            A
And I won't ever let you go.

               (A)   E   B
Chorus 4   And when I'm a - way, I will remember how you kissed me

                                   C#m
Under the lamp post back on Sixth Street,

                            A   N.C.
Hearing you whisper through the phone,   "Wait for me to come home."

PERFECT

Words & Music by Ed Sheeran

G   Em⁷   Cadd⁹   D   D/F♯

Capo 1

Verse 1
        G   Em⁷
I found a love for me,____
              Cadd⁹   D
Darling, just dive right in and follow my lead.
                 G   Em⁷
Well, I found a girl, beautiful and sweet,
           Cadd⁹   D
Oh, I never knew you were the someone waiting for me.

Pre-chorus 1
          N.C.   G
'Cause we were just kids when we fell in love,
                 Em⁷
Not knowing what it was,
          Cadd⁹   G   D
I will not give you up this time.____
                 G
But darling, just kiss me slow,
               Em⁷
Your heart is all I own,
           Cadd⁹   D
And in your eyes you're holding mine.

Chorus 1
          N.C. Em⁷ Cadd⁹   G
Baby, I'm dancing in the dark
            D   Em⁷
With you between my arms.
Cadd⁹   G
Barefoot on the grass,
D   Em⁷
Listening to our favourite song.
           Cadd⁹   G
When you said you looked a mess,
              D   Em⁷
I whispered underneath my breath.
           Cadd⁹
But you heard it,
          G   D   (G)
Darling, you look perfect tonight.

Link | G   D/F♯ | Em⁷ D | Cadd⁹ | D |

Verse 2
N.C.   G   Em⁷
Well, I found a woman, stronger than anyone I know,
                  Cadd⁹   D
She shares my dreams, I hope that someday I'll share her home.
                  G   Em⁷
I found a lover to carry more than just my secrets,
                  Cadd⁹   D
To carry love, to carry children of our own.

Pre-chorus 2
(D)   G
We are still kids but we're so in love,
                  Em⁷
Fighting against all odds,
                  Cadd⁹   G   D
I know we'll be alright this time.___
                  G
Darling, just hold my hand,
                  Em⁷
Be my girl, I'll be your man,
                  Cadd⁹   D
I see my future in your eyes.

Chorus 2
N.C. Em⁷ Cadd⁹   G
Baby, I'm   dancing in the dark
          D   Em⁷
With you between my arms.
Cadd⁹   G
Barefoot on the grass,
D   Em⁷
Listening to our favourite song.
          Cadd⁹   G
When I saw you in that dress,
          D
Looking so beautiful,
Em⁷   Cadd⁹
I don't deserve this,
          G   D   (G)
Darling, you look perfect tonight.

N.C. Em⁷ Cadd⁹   G
Chorus 3   Baby, I'm dancing in the dark
                       D   Em⁷
               With you between my arms.
               Cadd⁹   G
               Barefoot on the grass,
               D   Em⁷
               Listening to our favourite song.
                       Cadd⁹   G
               I have faith in what I see,
                              D   Em⁷   Cadd⁹
               Now I know I have met an angel in person.
                       G   D
               And she looks perfect,
                 Cadd⁹
               I don't deserve it,
               D   (G)
               You look perfect tonight.

Outro | G   D/F♯ | Em⁷ D | Cadd⁹ | D | G   ‖

142

RUNAWAY

Words & Music by Ed Sheeran & Pharrell Williams

Em   C   G   C6   Am   D   B7

Capo fourth fret

Intro

        N.C.   Em   C G
Mmm, mmm, mmm, ah.____

                   Em   C6 G
Mmm, mmm, mmm, ah.____

                   Em   C G
Mmm, mmm, mmm, ah.____

                   Em   C6 G
Mmm, mmm, mmm, ah.____

Verse 1

       Em
    I've known it for a long time,
       C   G
Daddy wakes up to a drink at night.
       Em
    Disappearing all night,
       C6   G
I don't wanna know where he's been lying.
       Em
    I know what I wanna do,
           C   G
I wanna runaway, runaway with you,
       Em   C6   G
    Gonna grab clothes, six in the morning,   go.

Pre-chorus 1

       Am Em   G   D
How long you leav - ing?
                  Am   Em   G   D
Well, Dad just don't expect me back this even - ing.
              Am   Em   G   D
Oh, it could take a bit of time to heal this,
              B7
It's been a long day, thumb on side of the roadway.

Chorus 1

N.C.   Em   C   G
But I love him from the skin to my bones,

           Em   C6   G
But I don't wanna live in his home.

           Em   C   G
There's nothing to say 'cause he knows

           Em   C6   G
I'll just run a - way and be on my own.

Verse 2

Em
    I've never seen my dad cry,

C   G
Cold as stone in the kitchen light.

Em
    I tell you it's about time,

   C6   G
But I was raised to keep quiet.

Em
    And this is what I'm gonna do,

      C   G
Gonna runaway, gonna make that move,

Em   C6   G
    Gonna grab clothes and when it's morning,   go.

Pre-chorus 2   As Pre-chorus 1

Chorus 2   As Chorus 1

Verse 3

(Em)   (C)
    Backpack and a flat cap turned to the back

       (G)
As I packed my clothes up,

(Em)   (C)   (G)
    My dad wasn't down with that plan to attack, intends to show love.

Em   C   G
    I don't wanna live this way, gonna take my things and go,

Em   C   G
    If things change in a matter of days, I could be persuaded to hold o

Am   Em   G
Our Mama was the same, but none of us are saints,

            D   Am   Em
I guess that God knows that   I don't wanna runaway

                   G   D
But one of these days I might just show that.

Am   Em   G   D
Put my home in a suitcase, tie both shoelaces, and hope that

B7
Things change, but for now I leave town

With a backpack on my shoulder.

N.C.   Em   C   G
I love him from the skin to my bones,

                              Em   C6   G
But I don't wanna live in his home.

                              Em   C   G
There's nothing to say 'cause he knows

                         Em   N.C.
I'll just run a - way and be on my own. Oh, mmm.

SAVE MYSELF

Words & Music by Ed Sheeran, Timothy McKenzie & Amy Wadge

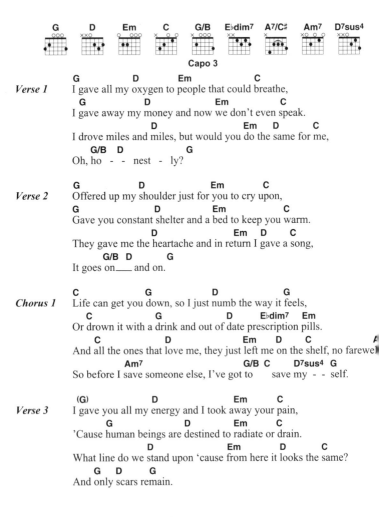

G D Em C G/B E♭dim7 A7/C♯ Am7 D7sus4

Capo 3

Verse 1
      G   D   Em
I gave all my oxygen to people that could breathe,
      G   D   Em   C
I gave away my money and now we don't even speak.
                        D   Em   D   C
I drove miles and miles, but would you do the same for me,
         G/B D   G
Oh, ho - - nest - ly?

Verse 2
      G   D   Em   C
Offered up my shoulder just for you to cry upon,
      G   D   Em   C
Gave you constant shelter and a bed to keep you warm.
                    D   Em D   C
They gave me the heartache and in return I gave a song,
        G/B D   G
It goes on___ and on.

Chorus 1
      C   G   D   G
Life can get you down, so I just numb the way it feels,
      C   D   E♭dim7 Em
Or drown it with a drink and out of date prescription pills.
        C   D   Em D   C
And all the ones that love me, they just left me on the shelf, no farewell
        Am7   G/B C   D7sus4 G
So before I save someone else, I've got to   save my - - self.

Verse 3
      (G)   D   Em   C
I gave you all my energy and I took away your pain,
         G   D   Em   C
'Cause human beings are destined to radiate or drain.
                      D   Em   D   C
What line do we stand upon 'cause from here it looks the same?
      G D   G
And only scars remain.

        (G)   Em   C   G
Bridge But if I don't, then I'll go back to where I'm rescuing a stranger,
                D   Em
Just because they needed saving, just like that.
                C   G
Oh, I'm here again, between the devil and the danger,
            D
But I guess it's just my nature.
            C   D
My dad was wrong, 'cause I'm not like my mum,
               Em   D   C   A/C♯
'Cause she'd just smile and I'm complaining in a song, but it helps,
            Am7   G/B C D7sus4 G
So before I save someone else, I've got to save my - - self.

        C   G   D   G
Chorus 3 Life can get you down, so I just numb the way it feels,
        C   G   D   E♭dim7 Em
Or drown it with a drink and out of date prescription pills.
        C   D   Em   D   C   A/C♯
And all the ones that love me, they just left me on the shelf, no farewell,
            Am7   G/B C D7sus4 G
So before I save someone else, I've got to save my - - self.
            Am7   G/B C D7sus4 G
And before I blame someone else, I've got to save my - - self.
            Am7   G/B C D7sus4 G
And before I love someone else, I've got to love my - - self.

SHAPE OF YOU

Words & Music by Ed Sheeran, Kevin Briggs, Steve Mac,
Kandi Burruss, Tameka Cottle, & John McDaid

Bm7   Em7   G   A   A#m7

Capo 2

Intro   ‖: Bm7 | Em7 | G | A   :‖

Verse 1
      Bm7   Em7
The club isn't the best place to find a lover,
       G   A
So the bar is where I go,
Bm7   Em7
Me and my friends at the table doing shots,
         G   A
Drinking fast and then we talk slow.
          Bm7   Em7
And you come over and start up a conversation with just me,
     G   A
And trust me I'll give it a chance now.
        Bm7   Em7
Take my hand, stop, put Van The Man on the jukebox,
       G   A
And then we start to dance and now I'm singing like,

Pre chorus 1
Bm7   Em7
'Girl, you know I want your love,
G   A   Bm7
Your love was handmade for somebody like me.
          Em7
Come on now, follow my lead,
G   A
I may be crazy, don't mind me.
      Bm7   Em7
Say, boy, let's not talk too much,
G   A   Bm7
Grab on my waist and put that body on me.
       Em7
Come on now, follow my lead,
       G   N.C.
Come, come on now, follow my lead.'

Bm⁷   Em⁷   G
    I'm in love with the shape of you,
               A   Bm⁷
We push and pull like a magnet do.
             Em⁷   G
Although my heart is falling too,
     A
I'm in love with your body.
Bm⁷   Em⁷   G
   Last night you were in my room,
            A   Bm⁷
And now my bedsheets smell like you.
               Em⁷   G
Every day discovering something brand new,
         A
Oh, I'm in love with your body.

Bm⁷   Em⁷
Oh I, oh I, oh I, oh I,
G   A
 Oh, I'm in love with your body.
Bm⁷   Em⁷
Oh I, oh I, oh I, oh I,
G   A
  Oh, I'm in love with your body.
Bm⁷   Em⁷
Oh I, oh I, oh I, oh I,
G   A   Bm⁷
  Oh, I'm in love with your body.
               Em⁷   G
Every day discovering something brand new,
     A
I'm in love with the shape of you.

	Bm7		Em7

Verse 2

Bm7   Em7
One week in we let the story begin,
          G   A
We're going out on our first date.
      Bm7   Em7
You and me are thrifty, so go all you can eat,
       G   A
Fill up your bag and I fill up a plate.
      Bm7   Em7
We talk for hours and hours about the sweet and the sour,
       G   A
And how your family is doing okay.
       Bm7   Em7
And leave and get in a taxi, then kiss in the backseat,
   G   A
Tell the driver make the radio play, and I'm singing like.

Pre-chorus 2 as Pre-chorus 1

Chorus 3 as Chorus 1

Chorus 4 as Chorus 2

Bridge

N.C.
Come on, be my baby, come on.

Come on, be my baby, come on.

Come on, be my baby, come on.
                     A♯m7
Come on, be my baby, come on.
Bm7   Em7
  Come on, be my baby, come on.
G   A   A♯m7
  Come on, be my baby, come on.
Bm7   Em7
  Come on, be my baby, come on.
N.C.
  Come on, be my baby, come on.

Chorus 6

    Bm⁷   Em⁷
    (Come on, be my baby, come on.)
    G   A
  (Come on) I'm in love with your body.
    Bm⁷   Em⁷
    (Come on, be my baby, come on.)
    G   A
  (Come on) I'm in love with your body.
    Bm⁷   Em⁷
    (Come on, be my baby, come on.)
    G   A
  (Come on) I'm in love with your body.
    Bm⁷   Em⁷   G
    Every day discovering something brand new,
      A   N.C.
I'm in love with the shape of you.

SHE

Words & Music by Ed Sheeran & Amy Wadge

G   B7   Em   A7   Am7   Bm7   Dadd4   C   Cadd9

Capo 2

Intro

| G | B7 | Em | A7 | |

| Am7 | Bm7 | Am7 | Dadd4 | |

Verse 1

G   B7   Em   A7
  I paid all my dues   and she wanted to know
Am7   Bm7   Am7   Dadd4
    That I'd never leave her,   now I'm ready to go.
G   B7   Em   A7
  And strange as it seems   she's endless to me,
Am7   Bm7   Am7   Dadd4
    She's just like paperwork,   but harder to read.

Chorus 1

C   Em   G   C
   And patience's my enemy   and loving's my friend,
                                                        Em
It's harder to leave with my heart on my sleeve
            G   Dadd4 C
Than to stay and just pretend.
D   G   B7   Em   A7
Oh, she knows me so well,
            Am7   Dadd4   G   Cadd9
Oh, she knows me like I know myself.

Verse 2

G   B7   Em   A7
  I made all my plans   and she has made hers,
Am7   Bm7 Am7   Dadd4
    She kept me in mind,   but I wasn't sure.
G   B7   Em   A7
  I searched every room   for a way to escape,
                Am7   Bm7   Am7
But every time I tried to leave she keeps holding on to me for dear life
                         Dadd4
And blocking my way.

       C   **Em**   **G**   **C**
And patience's my enemy   and loving's my friend,

                                  Em
It's harder to leave with my heart on my sleeve

          Dadd4
Than to stay and just pretend.

       G   **B7**   **Em** **A7**
Oh, she knows me so well,

        Am7   **Dadd4**   **G**   **Cadd9**
Oh, she knows me like I know myself.

(Cadd9)   **C**
And like the back of her hand, she already

          Em   **G**   **C**
Understands everything, won't you stay? And she says,

                            B7
And she already knows how it goes

                       G   **C**
And where she stands, I'll stay, anyway.

(C)   **Dadd4**   **Em** **G**
'Cause she knows me so well,

      C   **Dadd4**   **Em** **G**
Oh, she knows me like I know myself.

      C   **Dadd4**   **Em** **G**
Oh, she knows me so well,

      C   **Dadd4**   **Em**   **G**
Oh, she knows me like I know myself, I know myself.

      C   **Dadd4**   **G**   **C**
Oh, she knows me like I know myself,

         G   **C**
I know myself.

         G   **C**
I know myself.

         G
I know myself.

SHIRTSLEEVES

Words & Music by Ed Sheeran

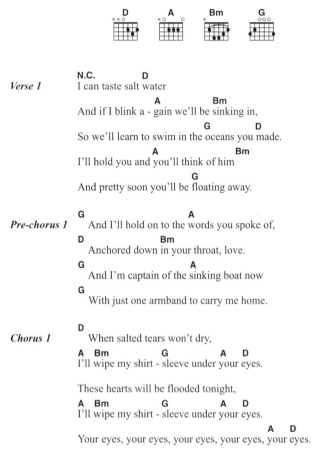

Verse 1

N.C.   D
I can taste salt water

           A   Bm
And if I blink a - gain we'll be sinking in,

                       G   D
So we'll learn to swim in the oceans you made.

           A   Bm
I'll hold you and you'll think of him

               G
And pretty soon you'll be floating away.

Pre-chorus 1

G   A
And I'll hold on to the words you spoke of,

D   Bm
Anchored down in your throat, love.

G   A
And I'm captain of the sinking boat now

G
With just one armband to carry me home.

Chorus 1

     D
When salted tears won't dry,

A Bm   G   A   D
I'll wipe my shirt - sleeve under your eyes.

These hearts will be flooded tonight,

A Bm   G   A   D
I'll wipe my shirt - sleeve under your eyes.

                                    A   D
Your eyes, your eyes, your eyes, your eyes, your eyes.

Verse 2

N.C.   D
I still taste salt water

          A   Bm
On my lips from your kiss, bitterness,

                       G   D
And I'll drown within the oceans you made.

                            A   Bm
And I hate to love you, these cuts are covered in your make-up,

                        G
I'll never trust you again, you can just be a friend.

Pre-chorus 2   As Pre-chorus 1

Chorus 2

D
  When salted tears won't dry,

A Bm   G   A   D
I'll wipe my shirt - sleeve under your eyes

These hearts will be flooded tonight,

A Bm   G   A   D
I'll wipe my shirt - sleeve under your eyes.

Bridge

G   A
Your eyes, your lips, your mouth your thighs, your back,

Bm   D   G
  You drive me wild to - night, the fact is I,___

                 A   Bm
I'm on the way home, I'm on the way home.

D   G
  I lied, I tried to cry but I'm,

    A   (D)
I'm drowning in the oceans you made.___

Instrumental ‖: D | Bm | G | A   :‖

Chorus 3

D
  When salted tears won't dry,

A Bm   G   A   D
I'll wipe my shirt - sleeve under your eyes.

These hearts will be flooded tonight,

A Bm   G   A   D
I'll wipe my shirt - sleeve under your eyes.

                                 A   D   (G)
Your eyes, your eyes, your eyes, your eyes, your eyes.

SMALL BUMP

Words & Music by Ed Sheeran

Capo third fret

Intro ‖: Em | Bm(♭6) Cmaj7 | G5 | G5 D/F♯ :‖

Verse 1
D/F♯   Em   Bm(♭6)   Cmaj7   G5
You're just a small bump unborn, in four months you're brought to li†
D/F♯   Em   Bm(♭6)   Cmaj7 G5
  You might be left with my hair, but you'll have your mother's eyes
    D/F♯   Em   Bm(♭6)   Cmaj7
I'll hold your body in my hands, be as gentle as I can,
        G5   D/F♯
But for now you're a scan of my unmade plans.
      Em   Bm(♭6)   Cmaj7   G5
That's a small bump, in four months you're brought to life.

Pre-chorus 1
(G5)   Am7   C(add9)/B   C   G5
I'll whisper quietly,   I'll give you nothing but truth,
                 Am7   C(add9)/B   C   D(add4)
If you're not in - side me,   I'll put my future in you.

Chorus 1
(D(add4)) Em   Bm(♭6) Cmaj7 G5
You are my one and on - ly
               D(add4)   Em   Bm(♭6) Cmaj7 G5
And you can wrap your fingers round my thumb and hold me   tig†
    D/F♯   Em   Bm(♭6) Cmaj7 G5
Oh, you are my one and on - ly,
              D(add4)   Em   Bm(♭6) Cmaj7 G5
You can wrap your fingers round my thumb and hold me   tight,

And you'll be all right.

Verse 2

N.C.	Em	Bm(♭6)	Cmaj7	G5

Ooh, you're just a small bump I know, you'll grow into   your skin.

Em   Bm(♭6)   Cmaj7   G5

With a smile like hers and a dimple be - neath your chin.

D/F♯ Em   Bm(♭6)   Cmaj7

  Fingernails the size of a half grain of rice

  G5

And eyelids closed to be soon opened wide.

Em   Bm(♭6)   Cmaj7   G5

A small bump, in four months you'll   open your eyes.

Pre-chorus 2

(G5)   Am7   C(add9)/B   C   G5

And I'll hold you tightly,   I'll tell you nothing but truth,

Am7   C(add9)/B   C   D(add4)

If you're not inside me,   I'll put my future in you.

Chorus 2   As Chorus 1

Bridge

D   Am7   Em

  Then you can lie with me with your tiny feet

G5   D

When you're half asleep, I'll leave you be.

Am7   Em

Right in front of me for a couple weeks

D/F♯   C   (Dadd4)

So I could keep you safe._____

Chorus 3

(D(add4))   Em   Bm(♭6) Cmaj7 G5

'Cause you are my one and on - ly,

D(add4)   Em   Bm(♭6) Cmaj7 G5

You can wrap your fingers round my thumb and hold   me   tight.

D/F♯   Em   Bm(♭6) Cmaj7 G5

You are my one and on - ly,

D(add4)   Em   Bm(♭6) Cmaj7 G5

You can wrap your fingers round my thumb and hold   me   tight.

And you'll be all right.

Outro

G5   Em   Bm(♭6)

'Cause you were just a small bump unborn for four months

Cmaj7   G5

Then torn from life.

Em   Bm(♭6)   Cmaj7   G5

Maybe you were needed up there but we're still un - aware as why.

SING

Words & Music by Ed Sheeran & Pharrell Williams

To match original recording, tune guitar down a semitone

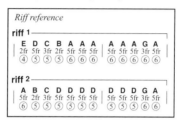

Intro | Am | Am | Am | Am ‖

Verse 1

N.C.   **Am (riff 1)**
It's late in the eve - ning, glass on the side,

     riff 1
I've been sat with you for most of the night,

Dm (riff 2)
Ignoring everybody here we wish they would disappear

   riff 2
So maybe we could get down now.

Am (riff 1)   **riff 1**
I don't wanna know if you're getting ahead of the pro - gram,

         Dm (riff 2)
I want you to be mine, lady, and to hold your body close.

       riff 2
Take another step into the no-man's land

For the longest time, lady.

Pre-chorus 1

   Am
I need you darling, come on set the tone,

If you feel you're falling, won't you let me know?

     Dm
Oh, oh-oh-oh, ooh-ooh, oh, oh-oh-oh, ooh-ooh.

cont.

Am
If you love me come on get involved,

Feel it rushing through you from your head to toe.

Dm
Oh, oh-oh-oh, ooh-ooh, oh, oh-oh-oh, ooh-ooh. Sing!

Chorus 1

Am (riff 1)
Oh, oh, oh, oh-oh, oh, oh, oh, oh, oh, oh, oh-oh.
riff 1
Oh, oh, oh, oh-oh, oh, oh, oh, oh, oh, oh, oh-oh. Louder!
Dm (riff 2)
Oh, oh, oh, oh-oh, oh, oh, oh, oh, oh, oh, oh-oh. Sing!
riff 2
Oh, oh, oh, oh-oh, oh, oh, oh, oh, oh, oh, oh-oh.

Rap

N.C.   **Am (riff 1)**
This love is a - blaze, I saw flames from the side of the stage

And the fire brigade comes in a couple of days.
          riff 1
Until then we got nothing to say and nothing to know,

But something to drink and maybe something to smoke.
Dm (riff 2)
    Let it go until our roads are changed,

Singing "We Found Love" in a local rave, no,
riff 2
I don't really know what I'm supposed to say

But I can just figure it out and hope and pray.
  Am (riff 1)
I told her my name and said, "It's nice to meet ya."

Then she handed me a bottle of water filled with tequila.
riff 1
I already know she's a keeper,

Just from this one small act of kindness
          Dm (riff 2)
I'm in deep, deep. If anybody finds out,

I'm meant to drive home but I've drunk all of it now.
      riff 2
Not sobering up we just sit on the couch,

One thing led to another, now she's kissing my mouth.

159

Pre-chorus 2   As Pre-chorus 1

Chorus 2   As Chorus 1

Bridge
        Am
Can you feel it?

All the guys in here don't even wanna dance.

Can you feel it?

All that I can hear is music from the back.
        Dm
Can you feel it?

Found you hiding here so won't you take my hand darling

Before the beat kicks in again?
        Am
Can you feel it? Ooh, ah, oh.
        Dm
Can you feel it? Ooh, no, no, no, whoa, no, no.

Chorus 3
N.C.   **Am (riff 1)**
Sing! I need you darling, come on set the tone,
       riff 1
If you feel you're falling, won't you let me know?
          Dm (riff 2)
Oh, oh-oh-oh, ooh-ooh.
       riff 2
Oh, oh-oh-oh, ooh-ooh. Sing!
Am (riff 1)
If you love me come on get involved,
       riff 1
Feel it rushing through you from your head to toe.
          Dm (riff 2)
Oh, oh-oh-oh, ooh-ooh.
       riff 2
Oh, oh-oh-oh, ooh-ooh. Sing!

SO

Words & Music by Ed Sheeran

G   Em   C   Gsus⁴   G⁵/F♯   D/F♯   Dsus⁴   Dadd⁴

Capo 3

Verse 1

    N.C.   G   Em
I'm filled up with doubt, I have to move home,
                  C   G
But I want to stay with you for all of the summer.
   Gsus⁴   G   Em
I have my plan that you won't remember,
                C   G
If you want to see the world then please ask your mother.

Pre-chorus 1

G⁵/F♯ Em   D/F♯   G   C
            And I cannot hold your hand to watch you go,
          Em D/F♯   G   D Dsus⁴
I am a liar   as you might know.
Em   D/F♯   C
     I need you now,   I need your touch and your lips,
Em   D/F♯   G
     I need your smile and your kiss.

Chorus 1

  (G)   Em
'Cause you're so cool, you're so beautiful
       C   D   G   D/F♯
You're so_ and you're so.
        G   Em
You're so cool, you're so beautiful
          C   G
You're so and you're so.

Link 1

  D/F♯   G   Em
Mmm,__ mmm,__
           C   G
Mmm,__ mmm.
  D/F♯   G   Em
Mmm,__ mmm,__
           C   G   Gsus⁴
Mmm,__ mmm.

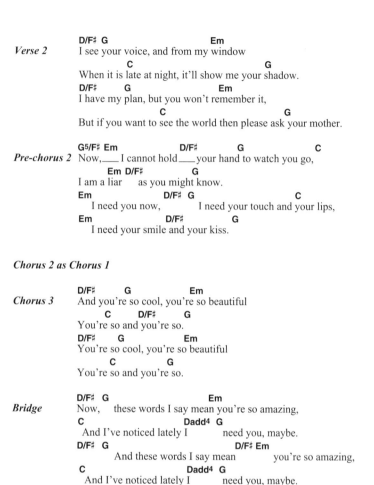

```
            D/F♯ G                        Em
Verse 2     I see your voice, and from my window
                         C                           G
            When it is late at night, it'll show me your shadow.
            D/F♯    G                     Em
            I have my plan, but you won't remember it,
                           C                         G
            But if you want to see the world then please ask your mother.


             G5/F♯ Em              D/F♯      G              C
Pre-chorus 2 Now,___ I cannot hold___your hand to watch you go,
                     Em D/F♯        G
             I am a liar    as you might know.
             Em               D/F♯ G              C
               I need you now,        I need your touch and your lips,
             Em                  D/F♯      G
               I need your smile and your kiss.
```

Chorus 2 as Chorus 1

```
            D/F♯      G           Em
Chorus 3    And you're so cool, you're so beautiful
                  C     D/F♯    G
            You're so and you're so.
            D/F♯    G            Em
            You're so cool, you're so beautiful
                  C          G
            You're so and you're so.


            D/F♯ G                         Em
Bridge      Now,   these words I say mean you're so amazing,
            C                   Dadd4 G
             And I've noticed lately I      need you, maybe.
            D/F♯ G                          D/F♯ Em
                 And these words I say mean      you're so amazing,
            C                     Dadd4 G
             And I've noticed lately I      need you, maybe.
```

Chorus 4

                D/F♯   G   Em
        'Cause you're so cool, you're so beautiful.
                    C   D   G
        You're so__ and you're so.
                D/F♯   G   Em
            You're so cool, you're so beautiful
                    C   G
        You're so and you're so.

SOFA

Words & Music by Ed Sheeran & Anna Krantz

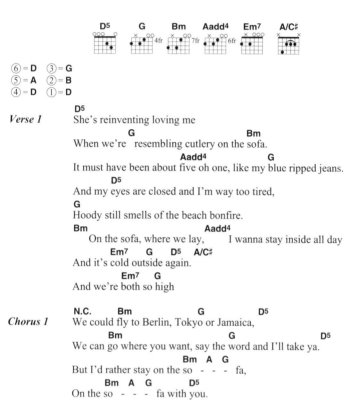

⑥ = D   ③ = G
⑤ = A   ② = B
④ = D   ① = D

Verse 1

D5
She's reinventing loving me
          G   Bm
When we're   resembling cutlery on the sofa.
                                Aadd4   G
It must have been about five oh one, like my blue ripped jeans.
          D5
And my eyes are closed and I'm way too tired,
G
Hoody still smells of the beach bonfire.
Bm   Aadd4
   On the sofa, where we lay,   I wanna stay inside all day
           Em7   G   D5   A/C#
And it's cold outside again.
          Em7   G
And we're both so high

Chorus 1

N.C.   Bm   G   D5
We could fly to Berlin, Tokyo or Jamaica,
       Bm   G   D5
We can go where you want, say the word and I'll take ya.
                             Bm A G
But I'd rather stay on the so   -   -   - fa,
          Bm A G   D5
On the so   -   -   - fa with you.

(D5)   **G**
   When the morning comes we're not watching Formula One,
Bm   **Aadd4**   **G**
   It's not what we breathe for, so kick off the day with Friends on T4.
D5   **G**
   Two, boiled and brew, two sugars ain't too sweet for you.
Bm   **Aadd4**
   On the sofa, where we lay,   I wanna stay inside all day,
       Em7 **G** **D5** **A/C♯**
And it's cold outside again.
       Em7 **G**
And we're still so high.

Chorus 2 as Chorus 1

Bridge

   G   **Aadd4**   **Bm** **D**
   And it feels like I'm flying,
   G   **Aadd4**
   And it feels like.

Chorus 3

   (Aadd4) **Bm**   **G**   **D5**
We could go to Berlin, Tokyo or Jamaica,
          Bm   **G**   **D5**
Through the streets of New York, that is where I will take ya.
      Bm   **G**   **D5**
Paris, Rome, to Rio, passing through Las Vegas,
      Bm   **G**   **D5**
We can go where you want, say the word, and I'll take ya.
N.C.   **Bm** **A** **G**
But I'd rather stay on the so - - - fa,
      Bm **A** **G**
On the so - - - fa,
      Bm **A** **G**   **D5**
On the so - - - fa with you.

SUNBURN

Words & Music by Ed Sheeran

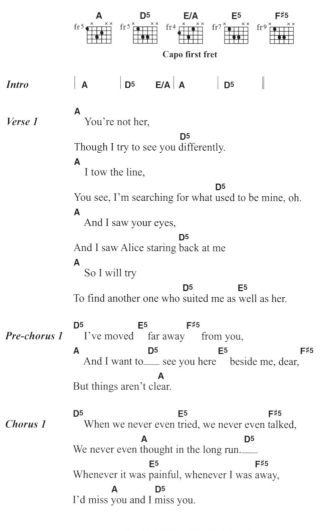

Capo first fret

Intro ‖ A | D5   E/A | A | D5   ‖

Verse 1

A
  You're not her,

          D5
Though I try to see you differently.

A
  I tow the line,

                              D5
You see, I'm searching for what used to be mine, oh.

A
  And I saw your eyes,

                    D5
And I saw Alice staring back at me

A
  So I will try

              D5   **E5**
To find another one who suited me as well as her.

Pre-chorus 1

D5   **E5**   **F♯5**
  I've moved   far away   from you,

A   **D5**   **E5**   **F♯5**
  And I want to__ see you here   beside me, dear,

                  A
But things aren't clear.

Chorus 1

D5   **E5**   **F♯5**
  When we never even tried, we never even talked,

              A   **D5**
We never even thought in the long run.__

              E5   **F♯5**
Whenever it was painful, whenever I was away,

          A   **D5**
I'd miss you and I miss you.

Verse 2

      A
     She was mine,

              D5
I was hers and all that's in between.

      A
     If she would cry,

              D5
I would shelter her and keep her from the darkness that will be.

Pre-chorus 2

          E5   **F♯5**
If I moved   far away   from you,

     A   **D5**   **E5**   **F♯5**
And I want to___ see you here   beside me, dear,

              A
But things aren't clear, woah.

Chorus 2   As Chorus 1

Bridge

      A
     Don't drop me in, it's not my turn.

D5
     If you cut deep then I might learn

        F♯5   **E5**   **A**   **E/A** **A**
That you   scarred and left me like sun - burn

Don't drop me in it's not my turn.

D5
     If you cut deep then I might learn

F♯5   **E5**   **D5**
     That you scar and leave me like sun - burn

Chorus 3

D5   **E5**   **F♯5**
When we never even tried,   we never even talked,

            A   **D5**
We never even thought in the long run.___

           E5   **F♯5**
Whenever it was painful, whenever I was away,

        A   **D5**
I'd miss you and I miss you.

SUPERMARKET FLOWERS

Words & Music by Ed Sheeran, Benjamin Levin & John McDaid

F   Am   B♭sus2   Dm   C   B♭   Gm   Am7

Capo 1

Intro | F   Am | B♭sus2 | F   Am | B♭sus2 |

Verse 1
             (B♭sus2) F   Am   B♭sus2
I took the supermarket flowers from the windowsill,
                     F   Am   B♭sus2
I threw the day-old tea from the cup.
Dm   C   B♭   F
    Packed up the photo album Matthew had made,
           B♭   C   F
Memories of a life that's been loved.

Verse 2
                  F   Am   B♭sus2
Took the 'get well soon' cards and stuffed animals,
              F   Am   B♭sus2
Poured the old ginger beer down the sink.
Dm   C   B♭   F
    Dad always told me, don't you cry when you're down.
                 B♭   C   F
But, mum, there's a tear every time that I blink.

Pre-chorus 1
Gm   B♭   F   C
    Oh, I'm in pieces, it's tearing me up but I know
Gm   B♭   F   C
    A heart that's broke is a heart that's been loved.

Chorus 1
    (C)   F   Am   B♭
So, I'll sing Hallelujah,
                  C   F   Am   B♭
You were an angel in the shape of my mum.
               C   Dm
When I fell down you'd be there holding me up.
B♭   F   C
    Spread your wings as you go
           Dm   B♭
And when God takes you back
           F   C
He'll say, hallelujah, you're home.

| F   Am | B♭sus2 C | F   Am | B♭sus2 |

'erse 2

(B♭sus2)   F   Am   B♭sus2
I fluffed the pillows, made the beds, stacked the chairs up,

C   F   Am   B♭sus2
Folded your nightgowns neatly in a case.

Dm   C   B♭   F
     John said he'd drive, then put his hand on my cheek

                    B♭   C   F
And wiped a tear from the side of my face.

're-chorus 2

Gm   B♭   F   C
     And I hope that I see the world as you did, 'cause I know

Gm   B♭   F   C
     A life with love is a life that's been lived.

'horus 2 as Chorus 1

nterlude

‖: F | Am7 | B♭ | B♭   :‖ *Repeat 3 times*
     Ooh._____

| Dm | C | B♭ | B♭ |
     Ooh. _____

'horus 3

F   Am B♭sus2
Hallelujah,

                                    F   Am   B♭sus2
You were an angel in the shape of my mum.

                                    Dm
You got to see the person I have become.

B♭   F   C
     Spread your wings and I know

                    Dm   B♭
That when God took you back,

                    F   C   F
He said, hallelujah, you're home.

TAKE IT BACK

Words & Music by Ed Sheeran & John McDaid

Verse 1

Dm
I'm not a rapper; I'm a singer with a flow,

I've got a habit for spitting quicker lyrics, you know.
                              B♭
You found me ripping the written out of the pages they sit in,
        C   C♯dim7
I never want to get bitten 'cause plagia - rism is hidden.
                    Dm
Watch how I sit on the rhythm, prisoner with a vision,

Signed to a label, but didn't listen to any criticism.
                  B♭
Thought you knew but you didn't, so perk your ears up and listen,
        C   C♯dim7
Studi - o is a system and you could say that I'm driven.
                  Dm
And now it's   on to the next saga, we drink the best lager.

I'll never try to win you over like your stepfather.
B♭
   I do my own thing now, and get respect after,
C   C♯dim7
   And I'm avoiding the 'caine like it was "Get Carter".
Dm
   For four years I never had a place to stay,

But it's safe to say that it kept me grounded like a paperweight.
      B♭
At sixteen years old, yeah, I moved out of my home,
        C   C♯dim7
I was Macy Gray, I tried to say goodbye and I choked.

cont.

Dm
I went from sleeping at a subway station,

To sleeping with a movie star and adding to the population.
      B♭
Not my imagi - nation, I don't wanna relax
        C   **C♯dim7**
Would it hurt your repu - tation if I put it on wax?

I take it back now.

Dm
Chorus 1   Mmm, come on and take it back love,
    B♭   **C**   **C♯dim7 Dm**
      Come on and take it back for us.

Don't you fade into the back love,
B♭   **C**
   No.____

C♯dim7   **Dm**
Verse 2   I take it back with the rhythm and blues,

With my rap pack I'll be singing the news.

Trying to act like Jack Black when I bring it to school,
B♭
I make a beat with my feet by just hitting the loop.
C   **C♯dim7**
Bringing the lyrics to prove that I can fit in these shoes,
Dm
I give you the truth through the vocal booth.

And stars burst out on the scene like an Opal Fruit,
      B♭
They try to take aim like Beckham when he goes to shoot,
      C   **C♯dim7**
But then a - gain that's what they're sup - posed to do.
          Dm
And I'm supposed to be calm, I tattooed the lyrics onto my arm,

Whispering: "Everything that happens is from now on."

B♭

I'll be ready to start again by the end of the song,

     C

Still they're claiming that I handled it wrong.

    C♯dim7   Dm

But then I've never had an enemy, except for the N.M.E.,

But I'll be selling twice as many copies as the magazines will ever be

B♭   C

With only spectacles ahead of me and festival fees

          C♯dim7

Are healthier than a Dalmatian on Pedigree.

Dm

Singing for the masses, rubber dinghy rapids,

I keep this rapping a habit and keep on fashioning magic.

B♭

I'm battling for respect, I don't know if I'll have it,

C   C♯dim7

This song's from the heart

                 (Dm)

Covers the planet, I'll take it back now.

Chorus 2   As Chorus 1

    C♯dim7

Verse 3   I take it back now.

Dm

Now I don't ever want to be perfect,

'Cause I'm a singer that you never want to see shirtless.

     B♭

And I ac - cept the fact that someone's gotta win worst-dressed,

      C   C♯dim7

Taking my first steps into the scene, giving me focus.

Dm

Putting on a brave face, like Timothy Dalton,

Considering a name change, thinking it was hopeless.

B♭

Rhyming over recordings, avoiding tradition,

        C

'Cause every days some lyrics and the melody could be written.

Dm
Now absence can make your heart ache,

But drinking absinthe can change your mind-state, vividly,

Need to let my liver be.
B♭
  And I'll say it again,
          C   **C♯dim7**
Living life on the edge, with a close handful of friends,
                          Dm
It's good advice from the man that took his life on the road with me,

And I hope to see him blowing up globally,
                    B♭
'Cause that's how it's supposed to be. I'm screaming out vocally,
           C   **N.C.**
It might seem totally impossible achieving life's dreams, but,
Dm
  But I just write schemes.

I'm never having a stylist, giving me tight jeans,
               B♭
Madison Square Garden is where I might be, but more likely
        C   **C♯dim7**
You find me in the back room of a dive bar with my mates
               Dm
Having a pint with McDaid, discussing records we made.

And every single second knowing that we'll never betray
               B♭
The way we were raised, remembering our background,
     C   **C♯dim7**
Sat down   that's how we plan it out; it's time to take it back now.

Chorus 3   As Chorus 1

              Dm
Chorus 4   Mmm, come on and take it back love,
           B♭   **C**   **C♯dim7** **Dm**
           Come on and take it back for us.

           Don't you fade into the back love,
           B♭   **C** **C♯dim7** **Dm**
           No._____

TENERIFE SEA

Words & Music by Ed Sheeran, John McDaid & Foy Vance

G5   A7sus4   C(add9)   Em7   G5/D   D5

Capo first fret

Intro
| G5 A7sus4 | C(add9) | G5 A7sus4 | C(add9) |

| G5 A7sus4 | C(add9) | Em7 G5/D | C(add9) |

| C(add9) ‖

Verse 1

G5   A7sus4   C(add9)
You look so wonderful in your dress,

G5   A7sus4   C(add9)
I love your hair like that.

G5   A7sus4   C(add9)
The way it falls on the side of your neck,

Em7   G5/D   C(add9)
Down your shoulders and back.

G5   A7sus4   C(add9)
We are sur - rounded by all of these lies

G5   A7sus4 C(add9)
And people who talk too much.

G5   A7sus4 C(add9)
You got the kind of look in your eyes

Em7   G5/D   C(add9)
As if no one knows anything but us.

Pre-chorus 1

C5   G5   G5/D
Should this be the last thing I see,

C5   G5   G5/D
I want you to know it's e - nough for me,

C5   G5   D5
'Cause all that you are is all that I'll ever need.

Chorus 1

(D5)   G5   A7sus4 C(add9) G5   A7sus4 C(add9)
I'm so in love,   so in love,

G5   A7sus4 C(add9)   G5   A7sus4 C(add9)
So in love,   so in love.

Verse 2

G5   A7sus4 C(add9)
You look so beautiful in this light,

G5   A7sus4 C(add9)
Your silhou - ette over me.

G5   A7sus4   C(add9)
The way it brings out the blue in your eyes

     Em7   G5/D C(add9)
Is the Tenerife Sea.

     G5   A7sus4   C(add9)
And all of the voices sur - rounding us here,

         G5   A7sus4   C(add9)
They just fade out when you take a breath.

G5   A7sus4   C(add9)
Just say the word and now we'll disappear

Em7   G5/D   C(add9)
Into the wilder - ness.

Pre-chorus 2   As Pre-chorus 1

Chorus 2   As Chorus 1

Bridge

Em7   C(add9) G5   G5/D
Lumi - ère,   dar - ling,

Em7   C(add9) G5
Lumi - ère over me.

Em7   C(add9) G5   G5/D
Lumi - ère,   dar - ling,

Em7   C(add9) G5
Lumi - ère over me.

Em7   C(add9) G5   G5/D
Lumi - ère,   dar - ling,

Em7   C(add9) G5
Lumi - ère over me.

Pre-chorus 3   As Pre-chorus 1

Chorus 3   As Chorus 1

Verse 3

G5   A7sus4   C(add9)
You look so wonderful in your dress,

G5   A7sus4 C(add9)
I love your hair like that.

G5   A7sus4   C(add9)
And in a moment I knew you, Beth.

THIS

Words & Music by Ed Sheeran & Gordon Mills

Capo fourth fret

Intro   ‖: G | G D(add4) | C | C D(add4) :‖

Verse 1
G   D(add4) C   D(add4)
This is the start of some - thing   beautiful,
G   D(add4) C   D(add4)
This is the start of some - thing   new.
      G   D(add4) C   D(add4)
And you are the one that'll make me   lose it all,
      G   D(add4) C
And you are the start of some - thing   new, oh.

Chorus 1
D(add4) Em
And I'll throw it all away
C   G   Em   C   G
   And watch you fall___ into my arms a - gain.
        Em
And I'll throw it all away,
C   G   C D(add4)
   Watch you fall,   now.

Verse 2
G   D(add4) C   D(add4)
You are the earth that I will   stand upon,
G   D(add4) C   D(add4)
You are the words that I will   sing, mmm.

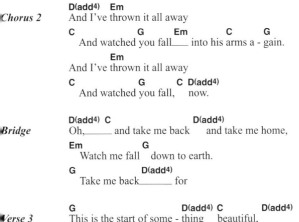

Chorus 2

    D(add4)   Em
And I've thrown it all away

C   G   Em   C   G
  And watched you fall___ into his arms a - gain.

                Em
And I've thrown it all away

C   G   C D(add4)
  And watched you fall,   now.

Bridge

D(add4) C   D(add4)
Oh,___ and take me back   and take me home,

Em   G
  Watch me fall   down to earth.

G   D(add4)
  Take me back_____ for

Verse 3

G   D(add4) C   D(add4)
This is the start of some - thing   beautiful,

G   D(add4) C
You are the start of some - thing   new.

THINKING OUT LOUD

Words & Music by Ed Sheeran & Amy Wadge

Verse 1

D D/F♯   G   A
When your legs don't work like they used to before

D D/F♯   G A
And I can't sweep you off of your feet.

D D/F♯   G   A
Will your mouth still remember the taste of my love?

D D/F♯   G   A
Will your eyes still smile from your cheeks?

Pre-chorus 1

(A)   D D/F♯   G A   D D/F♯ G A
And, darling, I   will be loving you   till we're seventy.___

                     D D/F♯   G A   D D/F♯
And, baby, my heart could still fall   as hard at twenty three.___

G   A   Em   A7   D
And I'm thinking 'bout how people fall in love in my - sterious way

Em   A7
Maybe just the touch of a hand.

         Em   A7   Bm
Well, me, I fall in love with you eve - ry single day

         Em   A7
And I just wanna tell you,___

Chorus 1

N.C.   D D/F♯ G
So honey oh,___

A   D D/F♯ G
Take me into your loving arms,___

A   D   D/F♯ G
Kiss me under the light of a thousand stars,

A   D D/F♯
Place your head on my beating heart.___

            G A
I'm thinking out loud

          Bm A   G   D/F♯ Em   A D
That maybe we found love right where we are.

Verse 2

D D/F♯   G   A
   When my hair's all but gone and my memory fades

D D/F♯   G   A
   And the crowds don't remember my name.

D D/F♯   G   A
   When my hands don't play the strings the same way,

      D D/F♯   G   A
Mmm,___ I know you will still love me the same.

Pre-chorus 2

(A)   D D/F♯   G A
'Cause honey   your soul could never grow   old,

                  D D/F♯ G A
It's evergreen,

             D D/F♯   G   A   D D/F♯
And, baby, your   smile's forever in___ my mind and memory.___

G   A   Em   A7   D
  I'm thinking 'bout how people fall in love in my - sterious ways,

Em   A7
Maybe it's all part of a plan.

     Em   A7   Bm
Well, I'll just keep on making the same mis - takes,

Em   A7
Hoping that you'll under - stand.

179

Chorus 2

N.C.   D D/F♯ G
But, baby, now,___

A   D D/F♯ G
Take me into your loving arms,___

A   D   D/F♯ G
Kiss me under the light of a thousand stars,

A   D D/F♯
Place your head on my beating heart.___

          G A
Thinking out___ loud

        Bm A   G   D/F♯ Em   A D
That maybe we found love right where we are.

Instrumental ‖: D D/F♯ | G A | D D/F♯ | G A   :‖

Chorus 3

(A)   D D/F♯ G
So, baby, now,___

A   D D/F♯ G
Take me into your loving arms,___

A   D   D/F♯
Kiss me under the light of a thousand stars,

        G   A   D D/F♯
Oh, darling, place your head on my beating heart.___

          G A
I'm thinking out___ loud

        Bm A   G   D/F♯ Em   A D
That maybe we found love right where we are.

        Bm A   G   D/F♯ Em   A D
Oh, baby, we found love right where we are.

        Bm A   G   D/F♯ Em   A D
And we found love right where we are.

TOUCH AND GO

Words & Music by Ed Sheeran & Foy Vance

Em   C   G   D   G*   G/B

Cadd9   D7   Em7   Em9   F   Am7

Capo 3

Intro

       N.C.   Em   C G D
Oh, ooh, oh-oh.

                Em   C G D
Oh, ooh, oh-oh.

                Em   C G D
Oh, ooh, oh-oh.

                Em   C G D
Oh, ooh, oh-oh.

Verse 1

       G*   G/B Cadd9
    Waking up,   midnight November
D   Em   C
   And you're still in my bed.
       G*   G/B Cadd9
   It's kinda rough,   'cause since I met ya,
D   Em   C
   There's things we've never said.

Pre-chorus 1

       (C)   Em Cadd9   D7 Em7 G/B C G/B Em9
So if I go___   for a little while longer,
                  Cadd9   F   C   D
When I'm home ___ we can talk about the pitfalls of the road.
       N.C.   Em C G D   Em   C G D
If you say go,   I would stop everything, oh,
                            Em   C G D
My heart would play the role now
                    Em   C G
And act like it's never been broke,   though my soul.

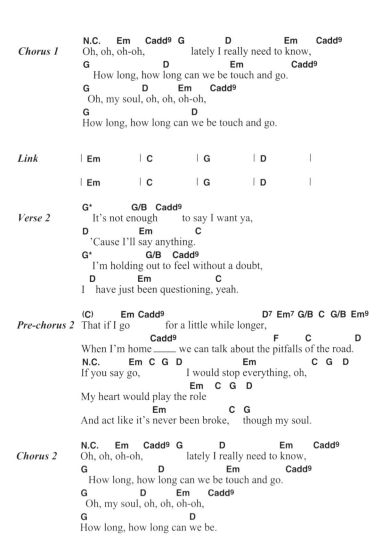

Chorus 1

```
            N.C.    Em    Cadd9  G            D              Em      Cadd9
            Oh, oh, oh-oh,            lately I really need to know,
            G              D                Em            Cadd9
              How long, how long can we be touch and go.
            G           D      Em     Cadd9
              Oh, my soul, oh, oh, oh-oh,
            G              D
            How long, how long can we be touch and go.
```

Link

```
            | Em        | C         | G         | D         |
            | Em        | C         | G         | D         |
```

Verse 2

```
            G*         G/B  Cadd9
              It's not enough      to say I want ya,
            D            Em           C
             'Cause I'll say anything.
            G*          G/B    Cadd9
              I'm holding out to feel without a doubt,
              D            Em              C
            I  have just been questioning, yeah.
```

Pre-chorus 2

```
            (C)        Em  Cadd9                     D7 Em7 G/B C G/B Em9
            That if I go      for a little while longer,
                         Cadd9                    F      C           D
            When I'm home ____ we can talk about the pitfalls of the road.
            N.C.    Em C G D            Em          C G  D
            If you say go,      I would stop everything, oh,
                                 Em   C G  D
            My heart would play the role
                           Em            C  G
            And act like it's never been broke,    though my soul.
```

Chorus 2

```
            N.C.    Em    Cadd9  G            D              Em      Cadd9
            Oh, oh, oh-oh,            lately I really need to know,
            G              D                Em            Cadd9
              How long, how long can we be touch and go.
            G           D      Em     Cadd9
              Oh, my soul, oh, oh, oh-oh,
            G              D
            How long, how long can we be.
```

Bridge
```
         D          G            Cadd9      G
All of my bones, they scream I'm right,
                 D          G         Cadd9  Em
If you're taking me home to stay the night,
         Am7        G/B          Cadd9
Darling my soul would heal.
```

Pre-chorus 3
```
         N.C.      Em C G  D              Em              C  G  D
If you say go,          I would stop everything, oh.
                               Em   C  G  D
My heart would play the role
                      Em                 C  G
And act like it's never been broke,      oh my soul.
```

Chorus 3 as Chorus 1

Outro
```
         | Em       | C         | G          | D         |
         Em  C     G                 D               Em  C  G  D
         How long, how long can we be touch and go.
         Em  C     G                 D               Em
         How long, how long can we be touch and go.
```

183

U.N.I.

Words & Music by Ed Sheeran & Jake Gosling

E   Emaj7   C♯m   A(add9)   F♯m11   B(add4)   B

Capo second fret

Verse 1

        E   Emaj7 E
I found your hairband on my bedroom floor,
                           Emaj7   C♯m
The only evidence that you've been here be - fore.
           A(add9)
And I don't get waves of missing you anymore,
E   Emaj7
  They're more like tsunami tides in my eyes.
        E
Never getting dry, so I get high,
               Emaj7   E
Smoke away the days never sleep with the light on.

Weeks pass in the blink of an eye,
             Emaj7   C♯m
And I'm still drunk at the end of the night.
             A(add9)
I don't drink like everybody else,

I tip it to forget things about myself.
E
Stumble and fall with the head spin I got,
          Emaj7
My mind's with you but my heart's just not.

Pre-chorus 1

F♯m11
                      A(add9)
  So am I close to you any - more, if it's over,
F♯m11
                            A(add9) B(add4)
  And there's no chance that we'll work it out?_____

Chorus 1   **(B)**   **E**
That's why you and I ended over U.N.I.,
     C♯m   **A(add9)**   **E**
And I said that's fine, but you're the only one that knows I lied.

You and I ended over U.N.I.,
     C♯m   **A(add9)**   **E**   **B**   **E**
And I said that's fine, but you're the only one that knows I lied.

Verse 2   **N.C.**   **E**
Everybody said we'd be together forever but I know that

I never wanna settle down,

Come around, break up the love like Lego now.
C♯m   **A**
Never wanna turn into another like you,

Sleep with my thoughts, dance with my views.
E
Everything's great but not everything's sure,

But you live in your halls and I live in a tour bus.

Now I'm in a position to be another stalker,

Like every thing I say seems to all sound awkward.

Like our last kiss it was perfect, we were nervous on the surface,
C♯m   **A**
And I'm always saying everyday that it was worth it,

Pain is only relevant if it still hurts.
    E
I for - get like an elephant, or we can use a sedative

And go back to the day we fell in love just on our first kiss.

Pre-chorus 2   As Pre-chorus 1

Chorus 2   Oh, you and I ended over U.N.I.,

        C♯m   A(add9)   E
And I said that's fine, but you're the only one that knows I lied.

      You and I ended over U.N.I.,

        C♯m   A(add9)   E
And I said that's fine, but you're the only one that knows I lied.

      E   C♯m A(add9) E
Link   Whoa, oh.

            C♯m A(add9)   E
Whoa, oh,   oh.___

      (E)   C♯m   A(add9)   E
Bridge   Because   if I was gonna go somewhere,   I'd be there by now
      F♯m11   A(add9)
   And maybe I can let myself   down, whoa.
      C♯m   A(add9)   E
   And I'm thinking that I'm unaware,

                            F♯m11
I keep my feet on the ground and keep   looking around
                    A(add9)
To make sure I'm not the only one to feel low.
            C♯m A(add9) E   B(add4)
Because if you want, I'll take you in my arms
                 C♯m A(add9) E   B(add4)
And keep you shel - tered from all that I've done wrong.
             C♯m A(add9) E   B(add4)
And I'll know you'll say that I'm the on - ly one,
          F♯m11
But I know   God made another one of me
     A(add9)   B(add4)
To love you better than I ever will.

        E
Chorus 3   'Cause you and I ended over U.N.I.,

        C♯m   A(add9)   E
And I said that's fine, but you're the only one that knows I lied.

      You and I ended over U.N.I.,

        C♯m   A(add9)   E   B E
And I said that's fine, but you're the only one that knows I lied.

WAKE ME UP

Words & Music by Ed Sheeran & Jake Gosling

Intro | A | A |

Verse 1
     A   D
I should ink my skin with your name

     A   D
And take my passport out again and just re - place it.

See, I could do without a tan on my left hand,

                   D
Where my fourth finger meets my knuckle,

     A   D
And I should run you a hot bath and fill it up with bubbles.

'Cause maybe you're lovable,

    E
And maybe you're my snowflake,

     A
And your eyes turn from green to grey,

           D
In the winter I'll   hold you in a cold place.

And you should never cut your hair

    E   A   D
'Cause I love the way you flick it off your shoulder.

              E   A   D
And you will never know just how beautiful you are to me,

              E   E
But maybe I'm just in love when you wake me up.

Verse 2

A
And would you ever feel guilty if you did the same to me,

D   E
   Could you make me a cup of   tea to open my eyes in the right way?

A
   And I know you love Shrek 'cause we've watched it twelve times,

D   E
   But maybe you're hoping for a fairy tale too.

        A
And if your DVD breaks today, you should've got a VCR,

D   E
   Because I've never owned a Blu-ray, true say.

       A
And now I've always been shit at computer games,

And your brother always beats me,

    D   E
And if I lost, I'd go across and chuck all the controllers at the TV.

     A
And then you'd laugh at me and be asking me

If I'm gonna be home next week.

        D
And then you'd lie with   me till I fall asleep

  E
And flutter eyelash on my cheek between the sheets.

D   E   A D
   And you will never know just how beautiful you are to me,

          E   A
But maybe I'm just in love when you wake me up.

Verse 3

A
And I think you hate the smell of smoke,

You must try to get me to stop,
D   **E**
  But you drink as much as me   and I get drunk a lot.
A   **D**
  So I take you to the beach and walk along the sand,____
D   **E**
And I'll make you a heart   pendant with a pebble held in my hand.
A
  And I'll carve it like a necklace so the heart falls where your chest is.
D
  And now a piece of me is a piece of the beach,
E   **A**
  And it falls just where it needs to be and rests peacefully,

So you just need to breathe
                D   **E**
To feel my heart against yours now, against yours now.
     D   **E**   **F♯m** **A**
'Cause maybe I'm just in love when you wake me up.
    D   **E**   **F♯m** **A**
Or maybe I'm just in love when you wake me up.
D   **E**   **A**
Maybe I fell in love when you woke me up.

WHERE WE LAND

Words & Music by Ed Sheeran & Amy Wadge

A   Dadd9/F♯   E/G♯   F♯m   E   D6

Capo 2

Intro ‖: A   Dadd9/F♯ | E/G♯ A | F♯m E | A   :‖

Verse 1

A   Dadd9/F♯ E/G♯   A
Treat me beneath this clear night sky
      F♯m   E   A
And I will lie with you.
A   Dadd9/F♯ E/G♯   A
I start to feel those butterflies
F♯m   E   A
When I'm next to you.

Chorus 1

D6   E
   Tell me your secrets,
F♯m
    Give me a friend,
D6   E   F♯m
   Let all the good times flood in.
    D6   E
Do I love you, do I hate you?
  F♯m
I can't make up my mind.
      D6   E   (A)
So let's free-fall and see where we land.

Link 1 | A   Dadd9/F♯ | E/G♯ A | F♯m E | A |

Verse 2

A   Dadd9/F♯   E/G♯   A
It's been this way since we were young,
      F♯m   E   A
We'll fight and then make up.
A   Dadd9/F♯   E/G♯ A
I'll breathe your air   into my lungs
F♯m   E   A
When I feel your touch.

Chorus 2

D6   E
  Tell me your secrets,
F#m   A
  Give me a friend,
D6   E   F#m
  Let all the good times flood in.
      D6   E
Do I love you, do I hate you?
  F#m
I can't make up my mind.
        D6   E   F#m
So let's free-fall and see where we land.

Link 2

(F#m) D   E   F#m   A
Da-da-da, da, da-da-da, da, da-da-da, da.
        D   E   F#m
Da-da-da, da, da-da-da, da, da-da-da, da.

Chorus 3

D   E
  Tell me your secrets,
F#m   A
  Give me a friend,
D   E   F#m
  Let all the good times flood in.
     D   E
Do I love you, do I hate you?
  F#m   A
I can't make up my mind.
        D   E
So let's free-fall and see where we land.

Outro

‖: A   Dadd9/F# | E/G# A | F#m E | A   :‖

191

YOU NEED ME, I DON'T NEED YOU

Words & Music by Ed Sheeran

Em   Gmaj7   Asus4   C   D   G   A

Intro | Em | Em | Em | Em   ‖

Verse 1

       Em
Now I'm in town, break it down, thinking of making a new sound,
Gmaj7
Playing a different show every night in front of a new crowd.
       Asus4
That's you now, ciao, seems that life is great now,
C   **D**
See me lose focus, as I sing to you loud.
       Em   **Gmaj7**
And I can't, no, I won't hush,
                        Asus4
I'll say the words that make you blush,
       C   **D**
I'm gonna sing this now.   Oh, oh.

Verse 2

Em
   See, I'm true, my songs are where my heart is,
G
   I'm like glue, I stick to other artists.
A
   I'm not you, now that would be disastrous,
C   **D**
Let me sing and do my thing and move to greener pastures.
Em
   See, I'm real, I do it all, it's all me,
G
   I'm not fake, don't ever call me lazy.
A
   I won't stay put, give me the chance to be free,
C   **D**
   Suffolk sadly seems to sort of suffocate me.

Em   G
   'Cause you need me, man, I don't need you,

                                    A
You need me, man, I don't need you,

                                    C
You need me, man, I don't need you at all,

                D   Em
You need me, man, I don't need you.

                                    G
You need me, man, I don't need you,

                                    A
You need me, man, I don't need you,

                                    C
You need me, man, I don't need you at all,

                D
You need me.

(D)   Em
I sing, I write my own tune and I write my own verse,

        G
Hell,   don't need another word-smith to make my tune sell.

A
Call yourself a singer-writer, you're just bluffing,

        C   D
Your name's on the credits and you didn't write nothing.

Em
   I sing fast, I know that all my shit's cool,

G
   I will blast and I didn't go to Brit School.

A
   I came fast with the way I act, right,

N.C.
   I can't last if I'm smoking on a crack pipe.

Em
   And I won't be a product of my genre,

        G
My mind will always be stronger than my songs are.

A
Never believe the bullshit that fake guys feed to ya,

C   D
Always read the stories that you hear on Wikipedia.

Em
   And musically I'm demonstrating,

G
When I perform live, feels like I am meditating.

Verse 3

Verse 4

    A
Times at the Enterprise when some fella filmed me,

   C   **D**
A young singer-writer like Gabriella Cilmi.

Chorus 2   As Chorus 1

    (D)   **Em**
Verse 5   'Cause with the lyrics I'll be aiming it right,

                    Gmaj7
I won't stop till my name's in lights

At stadium heights with Damien Rice.

        Asus4
On red carpets, now I'm on Arabian Nights,

          C   **D**
Because I'm young I know my brother's gonna give me advice.

    Em
Long nighter, short height and I gone hyper,

Gmaj7
Never be anything but a singer-songwriter, yeah.

Asus4
   The game's over but now I'm on a new level,

C   **D**
Watch how I step on the track without a loop pedal.

    Em
Verse 6   People think that I'm bound to blow up,

        G
I've done around about a thousand shows,

        A
But I haven't got a house plus I live on a couch,

    C   **D**   **Em**
So you believe the lyrics when I'm singing them out, wow.

                   G
From day one, I've been prepared with VO5 wax for my ginger hair,

       A   **C**
So now I'm   back to the sofa, giving a dose of what the future holds

           D
'Cause it's an - other day.

    (D)   **Em**
Verse 7   Plus I'll keep my last name forever, keep this genre pretty basic,

             G
Gonna be breaking into other people's tunes when I chase it

     A
And re - place it with the elephant in the room with a facelift,

C   **D**
Into another rapper's shoes using new laces.

       Em
I'm selling CDs from my rucksack aiming for the papers,

    G
Selling CDs from my rucksack aiming for the majors.

      A
Nation - wide tour with Just Jack, still had to get the bus back,

C   **D**
  Clean cut kid without a razor for the mustache.

    Em
Verse 8   I hit back when the pen hurts me,

   G
I'm still a choir boy in a Fenchurch tee,

      A
I'm still the same as a year ago, but more people hear me though,

  C   **D**
Ac - cording to the MySpace and YouTube videos.

    Em
I'm always doing shows if I'm not I'm in the studio,

G
Truly broke, never growing up call me Rufio.

A
Melody music maker reading all the papers,

   C   **N.C.**
They say I'm up and coming like I'm fucking in an elevator.

Em   **G**
Chorus 3   'Cause you need me, man, I don't need you,

            A
You need me, man, I don't need you,

            C
You need me, man, I don't need you at all,

      D   **Em**
You need me, man, I don't need you.

            G
You need me, man, I don't need you,

            A
You need me, man, I don't need you,

            C
You need me, man, I don't need you at all,

      D   **N.C.**
You need me, man, I don't need you.

WHAT DO I KNOW?

Words & Music by Ed Sheeran, John McDaid & Foy Vance

Verse 1

E   D♯m   C♯m
Ain't got a soapbox I can stand upon,
B A   G♯m A   B
But God gave me a stage,___ a guitar and a song.
E   D♯m   C♯m
My daddy told me, son,   don't you get involved
B A   G♯m   A   B
In politics, religions, other peoples' quarrels.

Pre-chorus 1

A   C♯m   B   E
I'll paint the picture, let me set the scene,
G♯m A   C♯m   B   E
I know when I have children, they will know what it means.
G♯m A   C♯m   B   E
And I'll pass on these things my family's given to me,
G♯m A   B
Just love   and understanding, positivity.

N.C.   E   D♯m   C♯m
We could change this whole world with a piano,
B   A   G♯m A   B
Add a bass, some guitar, grab a beat and away we go.
E   D♯m C♯m
I'm just a boy with a one-man show,
B   A   G♯m A   B
No university,   no degree, but Lord knows.
E   D♯m   C♯m
Everybody's talking 'bout exponential growth,
B   A   G♯m   A   B
And the stock market crashing and their portfolios.
E   D♯m   C♯m
While I'll be sitting here   with a song that I wrote,
B   A   G♯m A
Saying love could change the world in a moment,
      B   E   D♯m C♯m B
But what do I know? (Mmm.———————)
A   G♯m A
Love can change the world in a moment,
      B   E   D♯m C♯m B
But what do I know? (Mmm.———————)
A   G♯m A   B
Love can change the world in a moment.

          E   D♯m   C♯m
The revolution's coming, it's a minute away,
B A   G♯m   A   B
I saw people marching in the streets today.
E   D♯m   C♯m
  You know we are made up of love and hate,
B A   G♯m   A   B
But both of them are balanced on a razor blade.

                     A   C#m   B   E
Pre-chorus 2   I'll paint the picture, let me set the scene,
                     G#m A   C#m   B   E
                  I know,   I'm all for people following their dreams.
                       G#m A   C#m   B   E
                  Just re - remember life is more than fitting in your jeans,
                       G#m A   B
                  It's love   and understanding, positivity.

Chorus 2 as Chorus 1

                     A   C#m   B   E
Pre-chorus 3   I'll paint the picture, let me set the scene,
                       G#m A   C#m   B   E
                  You know   the future's in the hands of you and me.
                       G#m A   C#m   B   E
                  So let's   all get together, we can all be free,
                            G#m N.C.
                  Spread love   and understanding, positivity.

Chorus 3 as Chorus 1

                  N.C.
Outro   But what do I know?

Relative Tuning

The guitar can be tuned with the aid of pitch pipes or dedicated electronic guitar tuners which are available through your local music dealer. If you do not have a tuning device, you can use relative tuning. Estimate the pitch of the 6th string as near as possible to E or at least a comfortable pitch (not too high, as you might break other strings in tuning up). Then, while checking the various positions on the diagram, place a finger from your left hand on the:

5th fret of the E or 6th string and **tune the open A** (or 5th string) to the note (**A**)

5th fret of the A or 5th string and **tune the open D** (or 4th string) to the note (**D**)

5th fret of the D or 4th string and **tune the open G** (or 3rd string) to the note (**G**)

4th fret of the G or 3rd string and **tune the open B** (or 2nd string) to the note (**B**)

5th fret of the B or 2nd string and **tune the open E** (or 1st string) to the note (**E**)

E or 6th	A or 5th	D or 4th	G or 3rd	B or 2nd	E or 1st

Head

Nut

1st Fret

2nd Fret

3rd Fret

4th Fret

(B)

5th Fret

(A) (D) (G) (E)

Reading Chord Boxes

Chord boxes are diagrams of the guitar neck viewed head upwards, face on as illustrated. The top horizontal line is the nut, unless a higher fret number is indicated, the others are the frets.

The vertical lines are the strings, starting from E (or 6th) on the left to E (or 1st) on the right.

The black dots indicate where to place your fingers.

Strings marked with an O are played open, not fretted. Strings marked with an X should not be played.

The curved bracket indicates a 'barre' - hold down the strings under the bracket with your first finger, using your other fingers to fret the remaining notes.

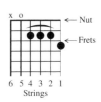

x   o   ← Nut

                              ← Frets

6 5 4 3 2 1
    Strings

Also available online and from all good music shops...

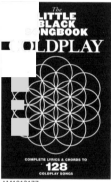
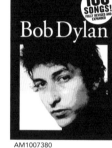
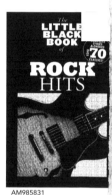